CW00690190

THE FRAZZLED PARENT

LEARNING 19 ESSENTIAL SKILLS TO TEACH YOURSELF
AND YOUR PRE-TEEN ADHD CHILD TO SUCCESSFULLY
NAVIGATE TODAY'S SHORT ATTENTION SPAN WORLD

ELAINE HOGAN

© **Copyright 2023 - All rights reserved.**

The content contained within this book may not be reproduced, duplicated or transmitted without direct written permission from the author or the publisher.

Under no circumstances will any blame or legal responsibility be held against the publisher, or author, for any damages, reparation, or monetary loss due to the information contained within this book, either directly or indirectly.

Legal Notice:

This book is copyright protected. It is only for personal use. You cannot amend, distribute, sell, use, quote or paraphrase any part, or the content within this book, without the consent of the author or publisher.

Disclaimer Notice:

Please note the information contained within this document is for educational and entertainment purposes only. All effort has been executed to present accurate, up to date, reliable, complete information. No warranties of any kind are declared or implied. Readers acknowledge that the author is not engaged in the rendering of legal, financial, medical or professional advice. The content within this book has been derived from various sources. Please consult a licensed professional before attempting any techniques outlined in this book.

By reading this document, the reader agrees that under no circumstances is the author responsible for any losses, direct or indirect, that are incurred as a result of the use of the information contained within this document, including, but not limited to, errors, omissions, or inaccuracies.

CONTENTS

INTRODUCTION

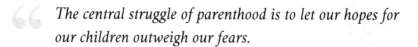 *The central struggle of parenthood is to let our hopes for our children outweigh our fears.*

— ELLEN GOODMAN

The struggle to balance our hopes and fears for our children is a major challenge for parents. Consider the case of a mother who was having difficulties with her pre-teen daughter who had ADHD. She recalls feeling overwhelmed and unsure of what to do the day she received the diagnosis. Raising a child with ADHD presents its own set of challenges, from managing their behavior to assisting them in developing life skills. However, as she learned more about ADHD and its effects on her child, she realized that her daughter's diagnosis was not a barrier to her future success.

This story serves as a reminder that while parenting a child with ADHD can be challenging, it can also be a journey of growth and self-discovery. The mother's experience emphasizes the importance of seeking out information and resources in order to better understand ADHD and its effects on her child. She discovered that her daughter's diagnosis was not a burden but rather an opportunity for her to learn and grow alongside her daughter through research and exploration.

According to the CDC (2021), an estimated 9.4% of children in the United States between the ages of 2 and 17 have been diagnosed with ADHD, with boys being more likely than girls to receive the diagnosis. The majority of those diagnosed have mild to moderate symptoms, and the average patient age at diagnosis is 7. Diagnoses and cases of ADHD have increased in recent years, with 11% of American children between the ages of 4 and 17 reporting the condition in 2011.

Increased research and resources are now being devoted to comprehending ADHD and offering support to those who are affected as a result of the rise in diagnoses. Despite this, a lot of families and individuals still find it hard to deal with the difficulties caused by ADHD, frequently feeling alone and overburdened. Beyond the diagnosed patient, the effects of ADHD extend to the entire family and their daily lives. However, people with ADHD can live happy and purposeful lives if the appropriate support and coping mechanisms are in place.

You are not the only parent going through this struggle. You're probably looking for solutions and tactics to control your child's behavior and aid them in developing the abilities necessary for success. This book provides you with exactly that. Your child's health, social skills, emotions, life skills, and behavior will all be managed through the use of action steps in this book which includes an overview of ADHD, a discussion of medication and natural treatments, and research-based strategies for managing your child's behavior and skills. You'll also find tips to help you take care of yourself as a parent and avoid neglecting your own health.

In order to give you the best information and recommendations, the author spent several months researching this book and consulting experts in psychology, education, and complementary medicine. A mother of three boys, one of whom has ADHD, the author has made herself an expert on the subject. With her first-hand experience and knowledge, she is motivated to help other families arm themselves with the information they need to help their children with ADHD succeed. She is particularly focused on assisting teachers and school administrators who are not fully equipped with the knowledge they need to deal with ADHD children.

You can help your child with ADHD and make parenting easier by reading this book to learn the shortcuts you need. With the right information and techniques, you can help your child acquire the abilities necessary for success while also taking care of yourself. The end result? A happier, healthier, and more fulfilling life for you and your child with ADHD.

1

TAKING A CLOSER LOOK AT ADHD

While ADHD is a term that is thrown into conversations regarding children, parenting, and education; it is often misunderstood or misdiagnosed. There are many stereotypes and discriminatory biases that come along with the diagnosis. It is not as simple as getting an answer to a problem when you finally figure out what is happening with your child. It probably feels scary, going into an unknown territory and trying to understand and help as much as you can without any real guidance. This is why researching, reading, and trying to get the right information about ADHD is so important. There are a lot of research papers and studies out there, but very few of them actually help since they are filled with so much scientific jargon.

Due to his impulsive actions and difficulty focusing, Leonardo da Vinci is frequently thought to have had ADHD. Despite these symptoms, he still managed to excel as a highly accomplished artist, inventor, and scientist. His famous works, like the *Mona Lisa* and *The Last Supper*, continue to be admired and studied. Additionally, his notebooks showcase his immense curiosity and creativity. Da Vinci's story serves as a source of inspiration and confirms that a diagnosis of ADHD does not have to limit one's success. In fact, his ADHD symptoms may have played a role in his unique perspective that led to his numerous achievements. This highlights the idea that individuals are unique and that an ADHD diagnosis should not be seen as a hindrance, but rather as a chance to work with strengths and overcome challenges.

WHAT IS ADHD?

Attention deficit hyperactivity disorder, or ADHD, is a neurodevelopmental condition that affects both children and adults. It is also the most prevalent mental disease diagnosed in youngsters. Symptoms include difficulties paying attention and regulating impulsive activities, as well as being overly active. ADHD is one of the most common neurodevelopmental diseases of children, according to the Centers for Disease Control and Prevention (2022), and it frequently persists into adulthood.

According to the American Psychological Association (2021), ADHD is a behavioral illness that makes it difficult for people to focus on daily requests and routines. It is usually diagnosed in youngsters, but it can last until maturity. Disorganization, impulsiveness, fidgetiness, and difficulties with concentrating and adapting to new surroundings are all symptoms of ADHD. These symptoms may appear around the age of seven, but not all children with ADHD will experience them all, and the severity can vary.

Furthermore, while some of these symptoms are normal for particular age groups, such as young children who are naturally energetic and curious, a child who exhibits a persistent pattern of these symptoms may have ADHD. To identify whether a child has ADHD, a professional evaluation by a physician, psychologist, or psychiatrist is required.

Misconceptions of ADHD

Despite major advances in science and a growing understanding of the neurological basis of ADHD, many myths and incorrect views about the illness persist in our society. With any disorder, these beliefs are reinforced by the media and older generations. These myths range from believing that ADHD is not a real condition to believing that it is caused by poor parenting or a lack of discipline.

Such myths and misconceptions can lead to confusion, stigma, and humiliation for people who have ADHD. It is critical to be informed and educated about the disorder, as well as recognizing that ADHD is a real disorder that requires proper acknowledgment, support, and treatment.

These are a few common myths that are often discussed in regard to ADHD, followed by the facts of the matter.

Myth 1: ADHD is not a real medical condition.

- **Fact:** ADHD is recognized as a real medical disorder by the National Institutes of Health, the Centers for Disease Control and Prevention, and the American Psychiatric Association. It is a widespread disease that affects millions of children and adults in the United States and has been proven to run in families. According to research, developmental abnormalities are seen in brain imaging of those who have ADHD (NHS, 2021).

Myth 2: Children can outgrow their ADHD diagnosis.

- **Fact:** It is normal for ADHD symptoms to persist in individuals as they age, and while some symptoms may lessen or disappear as sufferers learn how to manage them, the condition itself does not. Because most people with ADHD will continue to have symptoms into adulthood, it is critical to seek therapy to assist children in learning to control and minimize the symptoms rather than waiting for the problems to go away.

Myth 3: Only boys have ADHD.

- **Fact:** Because the symptoms of ADHD manifest differently in females than in males, girls are more likely to be missed and go untreated. Girls tend to be less hyperactive and have better impulse control, although they may appear more "daydreamy." The incidence of ADHD in girls and women has just lately been recognized by research. According to research conducted by Quinn and Madhoo (2014), girls and women with ADHD have the same impairments as boys and are more likely to have concomitant conditions such as oppositional defiance disorder, conduct disorder, scholastic and social impairments, driving problems, and risk-taking behavior.

Myth 4: ADHD is the result of bad parenting.

- **Fact:** ADHD is caused by brain variations, but it also has genetic and neurological causes. People frequently misdiagnose ADHD symptoms as a lack of discipline, while in fact, it is a medical illness. According to research on twins with ADHD, the home environment has very little influence on individual differences in ADHD symptoms (Livingstone et al., 2016). Although parenting practices do not cause ADHD, they can exacerbate concomitant diseases like oppositional defiant disorder (ODD) or conduct disorder (CD), and inconsistent parental discipline and poor paternal engagement have been linked to ADHD symptoms.

Myth 5: People with ADHD need to try harder.

- **Fact:** Individuals with ADHD, both children and adults, frequently try their hardest to pay attention, but their brains function differently, making it difficult for them to focus. Telling someone with ADHD to "just focus" is an ineffective remedy, akin to telling someone who is nearsighted to simply look farther. Their struggle to focus is not a reflection of attitude or effort; it is due to variances in the way their brain functions and is constructed. It is critical to remember that ADHD is a neurodevelopmental illness that cannot be conquered via willpower alone; it requires proper identification, support, and treatment.

Myth 6: ADHD is a learning disability.

- **Fact:** ADHD is not a learning condition, although it can impair a person's capacity to learn. ADHD symptoms can make it difficult for people to absorb and remember information, but they have little effect on specific skills such as reading, writing, and math. However, learning difficulties are prevalent in conjunction with ADHD, which may lead to the misunderstanding that ADHD is a learning disability. It's crucial to highlight that just because ADHD isn't a learning disability doesn't mean people who have it shouldn't get aid at school or work. They can get help managing and minimizing their symptoms, as well as adjustments to help them learn and achieve.

Myth 7: Special accommodations for ADHD are an unfair advantage.

- **Fact:** Special accommodations for ADHD children are not considered an unfair advantage because they are designed to level the playing field for those with disabilities, allowing them to participate in school activities and reach their full potential. These modifications, such as extra time on tests or a calm work environment, can reduce the impact of ADHD symptoms and allow sufferers to receive the same education as their classmates. They are not designed to provide an unfair advantage, but rather to provide those with ADHD some assistance in overcoming the hurdles connected with their disorder and achieving academic success. Individual accommodations are made and making them is a legal requirement under laws and regulations that protect people with disabilities from discrimination.

Myth 8: People with ADHD are stupid or lazy.

- **Fact:** People with ADHD are not necessarily "dumb" or "lazy." This disorder does not represent a lack of intelligence or work ethic. Individuals with ADHD may struggle with particular tasks, such as paying attention or being organized, but this is due to their disease, not their intelligence or motivation. Many people with ADHD are intelligent and motivated, but their symptoms might make it difficult for them to succeed in particular areas. Individuals with ADHD can overcome their obstacles and achieve success in school, work, and personal relationships with proper acknowledgment, support, and treatment.

Symptoms of ADHD

ADHD symptoms vary from person to person and can range from difficulties paying attention to impulsivity and hyperactivity. These symptoms can have a substantial impact on a person's capacity to function in daily life.

The symptoms of ADHD exist in three different types; to understand them we have to break down what each one is:

1. Predominantly inattentive presentation

This is characterized by attention and organizational difficulties. Individuals with this manifestation may exhibit symptoms such as forgetfulness, disorganization, and trouble following directions. They may also struggle with tasks that need persistent concentration and attention. This is exacerbated when a task is uninteresting or unengaging to them. They may put off things that demand a lot of mental work. Among these signs are:

- getting distracted by irrelevant sights and sounds
- having difficulty sticking to one job and frequently switching activities

- being forgetful and occasionally perplexed
- making careless errors
- struggling to focus and pay attention
- having trouble following directions, finishing work, and remaining organized
- losing track of personal belongings

2. Predominantly hyperactive-impulsive presentation

The predominantly hyperactive presentation of ADHD is diagnosed when five or more symptoms of hyperactivity/impulsivity and less than five symptoms of inattention have been observed in the past six months. These signs can lead to major challenges in a child's life, such as academic underachievement, poor social interaction with other children and adults, and behavioral issues. Adults with this diagnosis have fewer motor symptoms, but they still have restlessness and impulsive behavior. These are a few symptoms that may occur simultaneously.

- fidgets, taps his or her hands or feet, or squirms in his or her seat
- leaves seat frequently when remaining sitting is expected
- can be agitated at times
- is unable to play or participate in leisure activities calmly
- is frequently "on the move," acting as if propelled by a motor
- speaks excessively on occasion
- responds before a question is finished

- has a difficult time waiting their turn
- interrupts or interferes with others on a regular basis (inserts self into conversations or games)

3. Combined Presentation

This is the most common presentation style. It exhibits impulsive and hyperactive behaviors, as well as inattention and distractibility. People with mixed type ADHD display symptoms of both inattention and hyperactivity. A diagnosis can be made if a person under the age of 17 demonstrates 6 or more of the specified symptoms in one category in the last 6 months, or if an adult exhibits 5 of the symptoms.

People with combined-type ADHD are prone to being impulsive and energetic. They may struggle to reach their full academic or professional potential. Children with ADHD are more prone to suffer learning impairments, depression, anxiety, or behavioral disorders.

Symptoms Based on Age

Age also has an impact on the way ADHD symptoms manifest. ADHD is usually diagnosed by the time the child reaches adolescence. Adults with ADHD may have shown complicated indicators that were ignored early in life. There are three types of ADHD, each with distinct symptoms that may change with age. Children's and adults' symptoms differ and can be difficult to distinguish at times.

ADHD signs and symptoms vary with age. To determine if a child has ADHD, it's important to consult a doctor.

Preschool to grade two:

- difficulty following directions
- fidgeting and talking during quiet activities
- careless behavior
- grabbing things without permission
- difficulty remembering things
- overreacting to minor incidents

Grades three to seven:

- delaying tasks
- rushing through work
- careless mistakes in work
- slow working speed and unfinished work
- clowning around in class
- acting without thinking of consequences
- difficulty following multi-step directions

Teenagers and adults:

- Difficulty setting priorities and completing important tasks
- Forgetting to write down assignments or keep track of deadlines
- "Spacing out" and needing to re-read information
- Getting sidetracked from uninteresting tasks

- Difficulty making friends
- Taking risks without thinking about consequences.

Many of these symptoms can occur in children and teenagers who do not have ADHD, and a doctor can only make a diagnosis if the symptoms adversely impact the individual's life at home and at school.

Causes of ADHD

ADHD is a well-researched problem in the field of child and adolescent mental health. The condition's specific cause is unknown. ADHD is a genetic condition, according to the findings. It is a neurological disorder that affects the brain (ADDitude Editors, 2017; NHS, 2021). Many parents of ADHD children have experienced ADHD symptoms as children. ADHD is commonly seen among siblings from the same family.

It's not clear what causes the brain differences of ADHD; however, experts say these may be the common causes.

- **Genetics:** ADHD is thought to have a genetic component, and children with the illness have a 25% chance of having a parent who also has the condition (Faraone & Larsson, 2018). Multiple genetic variables may be handed down, affecting near relatives as well.
- **Brain injury:** ADHD symptoms can be caused by brain damage such as early trauma, infections, or disorders such as meningitis or encephalitis. Children who have had a traumatic brain injury may be more likely to

develop ADHD for up to ten years following the injury. Furthermore, ADHD may be associated with decreased activity in brain regions that control attention and activity levels, as well as dopamine deficits.

- **External factors during pregnancy:** Exposure to environmental pollutants such as lead can cause ADHD in certain people. A gestational parent's health and lifestyle problems during pregnancy such as poor diet or disease may also increase the chance of ADHD in offspring.

- **Alcohol and tobacco use during pregnancy:** According to Knopik et al. (2016), alcohol and tobacco use during pregnancy has been linked to an increased risk of ADHD in children. However, the precise cause of ADHD has yet to be determined.

- **Premature delivery and low birth weight:** Preterm newborns' brain development differs from that of full-term infants, making it easier for health-care workers to detect children at risk for ADHD and autism early on. To reduce ADHD symptoms in preterm and low-birth-weight infants, preventive and treatment methods are proposed.

What Doesn't Cause ADHD

- **Allergies:** Although allergies may result in hyperactivity and inattention, there is no evidence to suggest that they are the cause of ADHD. However, for individuals who already have ADHD, allergies may worsen their symptoms.

- **Playing video games:** While excessive video gaming has been associated with attention problems, it is not regarded as a cause of ADHD. Instead, it may worsen symptoms in individuals already diagnosed with ADHD.
- **Poverty:** Poverty has been linked to an increased risk of behavioral and mental health issues including ADHD, but poverty itself is not the cause of ADHD.
- **Stress or instability:** Despite stress and instability having an impact on a person's behavior and mental health, they do not cause ADHD. ADHD is a neurodevelopmental disorder that is believed to have a genetic basis.
- **Food additives:** The belief that food additives such as artificial colors or preservatives can cause ADHD lacks significant scientific evidence. Most studies have found no clear connection between food additives and ADHD.
- **Immunizations:** Despite some individuals linking vaccines to the development of ADHD, there is no causal relationship between the two, as supported by multiple studies (CHADD, 2019).

Case Study: Frank

Meet Frank, a tween who struggles with inattentive ADHD. Frank often feels like his mind is wandering, and he has trouble focusing on the task at hand, even when it's something he enjoys. He is often easily distracted, and he has difficulty following through on instructions, even when he understands them.

At school, Frank finds it difficult to pay attention during class and to complete his homework. He often forgets to turn in assignments and has trouble staying organized. Frank also has a hard time making and maintaining friendships, as his inattention can make him seem disinterested or aloof to his peers.

Despite these challenges, Frank is determined to find ways to manage his ADHD and succeed in life. With the help of his parents, teachers, and a therapist, Frank is learning strategies to help him stay focused and organized. He is also practicing social skills to help him build and maintain meaningful relationships with others. With hard work and persistence, Frank knows that he can overcome his inattentive ADHD and achieve his goals.

Activity: ADHD Quiz

As you go through the quiz, consider each question or statement and think about how it relates to your child's behavior. If you answer "yes" to many of the questions or statements, your child may benefit from a professional evaluation to determine if they have ADHD.

Here's the quiz:

1. Does your child have trouble paying attention in class or at home?
2. Do they often forget important things, like homework or items they need for school?
3. Do they have trouble following through with tasks and completing projects?
4. Are they easily distracted by their surroundings or activities going on around them?
5. Do they have difficulty sitting still and often fidget or squirm in their seat?
6. Do they act impulsively without thinking things through first?
7. Are they frequently interrupting others or interrupting their own thoughts to move on to something else?

Remember, the purpose of this quiz is to provide you with a general idea of whether your child may have ADHD. Only a licensed health-care professional can make an official diagnosis. We hope that this quiz is a helpful starting point for you and your family.

Now that you have a comprehensive overview of ADHD, including its definition, common misconceptions, symptoms, and potential causes, you can call yourself a little bit of an expert. You also know the symptoms of ADHD based on different age groups, so you understand the unique challenges faced by children, adolescents, and adults with ADHD. From this information, you now have an understanding of what

ADHD is and the various symptoms that individuals with ADHD may experience, as well as ways to confidently separate fact from fiction when it comes to ADHD. You even know possible origins of the disorder through the causes of ADHD.

In the next chapter, we will delve deeper into the topic of ADHD treatment, exploring the different options available to those with ADHD, including both pharmacological and behavioral interventions. We will weigh the pros and cons of each treatment option and help you make informed decisions about the best approach for your specific needs.

2

WEIGHING YOUR OPTIONS–WAYS TO TREAT ADHD

P arents of preteens with ADHD are often faced with the difficult task of deciding how best to treat it. There are various options available, from medications to coping strategies, and it can be hard to determine which one is right for your child. Diagnosing ADHD can be a complex process and typically involves a thorough evaluation by a qualified health-care professional. This process includes a complete medical examination, an assessment of the child's developmental, educational, and psychological history, and a review of the child's symptoms.

In recent years, technology has opened up new possibilities for detecting and treating ADHD. According to one study, a virtual reality game could be used to detect ADHD. The game was created to test attention, impulsivity, and hyperactivity, all of which are symptoms of ADHD. The game's results corresponded with other well-established ADHD exams, indicating the game's ability to objectively diagnose ADHD. This is crucial because it provides a new and potentially more accessible technique of diagnosing ADHD while removing the subjectivity that might accompany existing diagnostic methods. In addition, the game gives an objective measure of ADHD symptoms, which might be useful in tracking treatment progress.

This chapter will provide a comprehensive overview of the diagnosis and treatment of ADHD. It will provide an overview of the different options available (including the importance of regular monitoring and adjusting the treatment plan as needed) and how parents can stay informed about new developments in the field of ADHD.

HOW IS ADHD DIAGNOSED?

A mental health expert, such as a psychiatrist, psychologist, or social worker, is often used to diagnose ADHD. They will aim to understand the patient's medical history, family dynamics, and behavioral patterns during the diagnosing process in order to make an informed judgment on a diagnosis.

ADHD is often diagnosed by a multi-step process that includes a comprehensive evaluation by a competent health expert. The goal is to rule out other probable sources of the symptoms and see if they are consistent with ADHD symptoms. Interviews, questionnaires, observations, and assessments are commonly used in the diagnostic process.

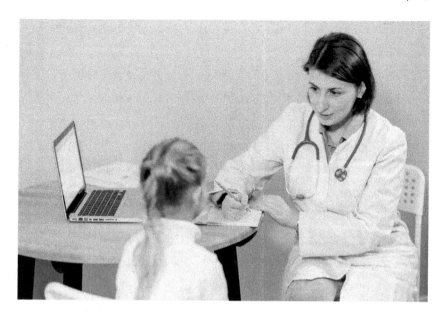

The process of diagnosing ADHD typically involves several steps.

1. **Initial evaluation:** A health-care practitioner, such as a doctor, will perform a physical examination on the child and examine his or her medical, developmental, and educational background. The health-care expert will also acquire information about the child's symptoms and behaviors from parents, teachers, and caregivers.

2. **Assessment of symptoms:** The health-care expert will assess the child's symptoms of inattention, hyperactivity, and impulsivity using established rating scales and questionnaires. These evaluations will assist in determining whether the child's symptoms match the criteria for an ADHD diagnosis as defined by the

Diagnostic and Statistical Manual of Mental Disorders (DSM-5).

3. **Rule out other possible causes:** Any other probable reasons for the child's symptoms, such as a learning disability, depression, or anxiety, will be ruled out by the health-care expert. Additional testing, including hearing and vision tests, may be performed to rule out any other probable reasons.

4. **Diagnosis and treatment planning:** Following the assessment, the health-care expert will make a diagnosis, and if necessary, propose a treatment plan. A mix of treatment, medication, and behavior-management measures may be used. The health-care expert will also educate and help the preteen's parents to support the child's needs and manage ADHD symptoms.

5. **Monitoring and follow-up:** The health-care expert will monitor the child's progress and make any necessary adjustments to the treatment plan. They will also offer parents and caregivers continuing education and assistance to help them understand their child's condition and how to best support them.

It is crucial to remember that the diagnosing procedure may differ based on the health-care expert, the child's age and symptoms, and other circumstances. As a result, it's critical for parents to collaborate closely with the health-care provider to ensure that the diagnosis and treatment plan are suited to their child's specific requirements.

Challenges When Diagnosing ADHD

ADHD in preteens can be difficult to diagnose for a variety of reasons. One significant challenge is that the symptoms of ADHD might be confused with those of other problems such as anxiety, sadness, or a learning disability. As a result, before making an ADHD diagnosis, a health-care provider may need to rule out other probable explanations of the child's symptoms.

These are some of the challenges commonly faced when diagnosing ADHD in preteens.

- **Difficulty in distinguishing ADHD symptoms from other conditions:** Symptoms of ADHD can be similar to those of other conditions such as anxiety, depression, or a learning disorder. This can make it difficult for health-care professionals to determine if a child truly meets the criteria for an ADHD diagnosis.
- **Variation in symptoms:** ADHD symptoms can vary greatly between individuals and fluctuate over time. This can make determining if a child's symptoms are compatible with an ADHD diagnosis challenging, especially for preteens who are still developing and changing.
- **Limited availability of specialized assessments:** Some health-care practitioners may lack the necessary knowledge to accurately identify ADHD in preteens due to restricted resources and a lack of specialized evaluations or diagnostic tools.

- **Stigma and resistance:** Parents and caregivers may have unfavorable perceptions about ADHD, be resistant to obtaining assistance, or be unaware that their kid has ADHD. They may also be opposed to medicine as a therapy choice.
- **Difficulty in communicating with parents:** When identifying a preteen with ADHD, communication with parents might be difficult. Parents may be concerned or unwilling to accept the diagnosis, or they may not completely comprehend the consequences of the diagnosis.
- **Lack of consistency in diagnosis:** ADHD is diagnosed by using a mix of characteristics such as symptoms, observations, and reports from parents and teachers. This can lead to inconsistencies in ADHD diagnosis and therapy for preteens.

HOW IS ADHD TREATED?

Medication, lifestyle adjustments, behavior control, and family support are common components of ADHD pre-teen treatment. When choosing a treatment plan for their kid, it is critical that parents understand the numerous alternatives available, investigate their effectiveness, and make an informed decision. Furthermore, parents must be aware of the potential adverse effects of each plan and be actively involved in their child's treatment process.

Medications such as stimulants, non-stimulants, and antidepressants are the most commonly used therapies for ADHD.

Finding suitable therapy for ADHD can be difficult, but working together with a skilled health-care practitioner to establish a plan that best meets the child's requirements is critical.

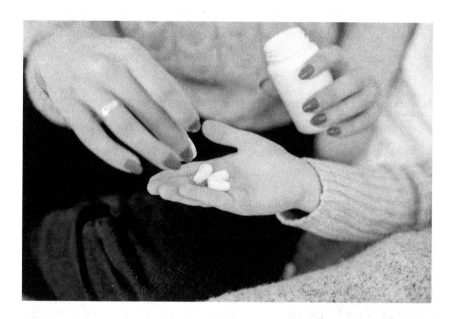

Here are several treatment options available for ADHD in children.

- **Medication:** Medicine is frequently used as the first line of therapy for preteens with ADHD, but finding the proper medication, dose, and timing to meet the child's particular requirements is critical. The most typically recommended drugs for ADHD in children are stimulant medications such as Ritalin and Adderall. These drugs boost concentration and attention by raising the amounts of specific neurotransmitters in the brain.

- **Behavioral therapy:** Behavioral therapy can also help preteens learn how to regulate their symptoms, improve their conduct, and develop social skills. Behavioral therapy is a type of treatment that teaches children how to control their symptoms and improve their conduct. Techniques such as parent training and training in social and organizational skills may be included.
- **Natural remedies:** Some parents may prefer to try natural remedies to treat their child's ADHD. These can include dietary changes, supplements, and alternative therapies such as acupuncture or yoga.

The approach to therapy for preteens is largely the same as for children. However, it is crucial to remember that preteens are going through substantial developmental changes, and their symptoms may vary and evolve over time. So, the treatment strategy should be flexible and adaptive. Parents of preteens with ADHD may expect to be included in the treatment process, and they can help their kid control the symptoms. Parents should also be informed of their child's medication and its side effects, and they should work closely with their child's health-care provider to evaluate their child's development and change the treatment plan as required.

Medication

Stimulant drugs such as Ritalin, Adderall, and Concerta are the most widely recommended treatments for ADHD in preteens.

These drugs boost concentration and attention by raising the amounts of particular neurotransmitters in the brain, such as dopamine and norepinephrine.

One of the primary advantages of ADHD medication for preteens is that it can help them perform better in school and other everyday activities. With fewer symptoms, preteens can focus better in class, finish activities more effectively, and follow directions more easily. Medication can also help with social skills and conduct, which can lead to improved connections with peers and adults.

However, there are certain disadvantages to using medication to treat preteens with ADHD. One of the biggest concerns is the possibility of side effects such as reduced appetite, sleeplessness, and gastrointestinal issues. Furthermore, preteens may build a tolerance to the medicine with time, requiring them to raise their dosages to attain the same results. Long-term prescription stimulant usage can also result in stunted development in preteens.

Stimulants and non-stimulants are the two most prevalent forms of medicine used to treat ADHD in preteens. Stimulants are the most typically recommended drugs for ADHD.

Examples of stimulant medications include:

- methylphenidate (Ritalin, Concerta)
- lisdexamfetamine (Vyvanse)
- dexamfetamine (Dexedrine, Dextroamphetamine)

These drugs can help preteens with ADHD reduce their symptoms of inattention, impulsivity, and hyperactivity. However, there are also drawbacks to drug therapy for preteens with ADHD, such as decreased appetite, sleeplessness, gastrointestinal difficulties, and pre-teen developmental issues.

Non-stimulant medicines are another type of ADHD treatment. These drugs, such as atomoxetine (Strattera) and guanfacine (Intuniv, Tenex), function differently than stimulants and can be beneficial in reducing symptoms in children who do not respond well to stimulants or who experience negative effects from them. They can also be taken in conjunction with stimulants to alleviate ADHD symptoms.

Therapy

Therapy is an essential part of ADHD treatment in preteens because it can help them control and decrease their symptoms, as well as increase their capacity to function in daily life. Special education, behavior modification, psychotherapy (counseling), and social skills training are among therapies that can be used to treat ADHD in preteens. Each style of treatment has its own method and benefits and may be adjusted to the child's specific requirements.

- **Special Education**

Special education is a type of therapy for preteens with ADHD that involves specific training, accommodations, and adaptations to assist the kid in academic success. Personalized education plans (IEPs) and 504 plans may be used, as well as small-group instructions, hands-on activities, and individualized instruction. Special education programs provide preteens suffering from ADHD with tools and methods to control their symptoms and increase their learning abilities, such as a calm work environment, task breaks, and visual aids for organization and recall.

- **Behavior Modification**

Positive reinforcement, incentives, punishments, and strategies such as token economies and self-monitoring are used in behavior modification treatment to change behaviors related with ADHD. This sort of treatment teaches preteens new skills and methods for controlling symptoms and improving everyday functioning, such as taking breaks, managing time, and being more organized.

- **Psychotherapy (Counseling)**

Counseling or psychotherapy is a sort of therapy that addresses the emotional and psychological elements of ADHD. This therapy provides preteens suffering from ADHD with talk therapy, cognitive-behavioral therapy, and family counseling to help them manage their conditions. It teaches children how to control their symptoms, regulate their emotions, deal with stress, and communicate properly. Psychotherapy is critical to increasing the capacity of preteens to function in daily life.

- **Social Skills Training**

Social skills training is a sort of treatment that focuses on assisting preteens with ADHD in developing the social skills required to function in daily life. This sort of treatment may include teaching the kid how to connect with people, begin and maintain conversations, and interpret social signs. Social skills training can assist preteens with ADHD by giving them the tools and tactics they need to navigate social settings and enhance their ability to communicate with others.

Natural Remedies

When it comes to treating ADHD in preteens, parents have a number of alternatives. Natural therapies are possible, and they are becoming increasingly popular among parents searching for alternate methods to manage their child's symptoms. Natural remedies should always be used in conjunction with other treatments, such as therapy or medicine, and should always be reviewed with a health-care practitioner.

- **Dietary Supplements**

Dietary supplements, including omega-3 fatty acids, zinc, and iron, are frequently advised as a natural ADHD treatment. Children with ADHD have reduced amounts of certain critical fatty acids and minerals in their blood, and supplementing with these nutrients helps to alleviate symptoms. It is crucial to highlight, however, that further study is required to validate these findings and identify the optimum dose for treating

ADHD (Sinn, 2008). Also, parents should be aware that dietary supplements are not regulated by the FDA in the same way that medicines are, so it is critical to pick a recognized brand and consult with a health-care expert before using supplements.

- **Herbal Medicines**

Herbal medications such as *ginkgo biloba*, St. John's wort, and ginseng are occasionally utilized as natural ADHD treatments. Some studies have suggested that these herbs may help with ADHD symptoms, but the data is conflicting and further study is needed (Bae et al., 2019). Also, parents should be aware that herbal medicines might mix with other prescriptions and may have negative effects; therefore, it is critical to consult with a health-care expert before using herbal medicines.

- **Music Therapy**

Music therapy is a type of treatment that uses music to enhance healing and mental wellness. Music therapy has been shown in certain trials to be useful in treating ADHD symptoms, particularly in terms of enhancing attention and lowering hyperactivity (Zhang et al., 2017). Music therapy can be combined with other types of treatment, like medicine and behavioral therapy.

- **Lifestyle Changes**

Changes in lifestyle, such as nutrition, sleep, and exercise, can also be useful in addressing ADHD symptoms. A diet that is heavy in protein and low in sugar, for example, can help to increase attention and minimize hyperactivity. A good night's sleep and regular exercise can also help to alleviate symptoms by increasing general health and well-being. Although these modifications will not cure ADHD, they may help to alleviate symptoms and minimize the need for medication.

Other Ways of Managing ADHD

Other types of treatment, in addition to medication, counseling, and natural therapies, can be used to control ADHD in preteens. Medical gadgets, support groups, and education are examples of these. Each of these types of therapy can offer preteens with ADHD and their families more support and resources.

- **Medical devices:** Neurofeedback monitors brain activity via sensors and provides feedback to the user, allowing them to learn how to regulate their brain activity. Electrical brain stimulation uses a modest electrical current to stimulate particular parts of the brain, which can increase focus and attention.
- **Support groups:** Support groups can be a valuable resource for preteens with ADHD and their families. They can provide a safe and supportive environment where individuals can share their experiences and offer support to one another. Support groups can also provide information and resources for managing ADHD and connecting with other families and professionals in the field.

- **Education:** Preteens with ADHD may need certain education programs and accommodations to succeed in school. This might include extra help from a teacher or a special education resource teacher, as well as accommodations like more time on tests or a quiet space to work.

It's crucial to note that treating ADHD in preteens is a complicated process that may need a combination of different treatment approaches. Each preteen with ADHD is unique, and different therapies may work differently for them. It is critical to collaborate with a health-care practitioner to determine the optimal treatment approach for your preteen.

Case Study: Timmy's Treatment

Timmy was a young boy who struggled with ADHD and had a difficult time focusing in school. His parents tried various treatments but none of them seemed to work. Then, Timmy's mother read an article about how music can help children with ADHD and decided to enroll him in piano lessons. Timmy was initially uninterested in playing the piano, but as he progressed in his lessons, he became fascinated with the instrument and the different sounds he could produce.

His piano skills improved, and so did his behavior in school. He was better able to focus and was no longer disruptive in class. Timmy's parents were amazed by the positive impact of the piano lessons on their son's ADHD symptoms. Timmy's piano teacher also noticed the benefits and included mindfulness activities in his lessons to help Timmy be more present and focused. Piano lessons became a crucial part of Timmy's routine and helped him manage his condition effectively. Timmy's parents noticed the positive impact of music, and they were grateful for it.

3

PARENTING HACKS FOR RAISING YOUR TWEEN WITH ADHD

R ecognizing that "failure" should not be part of your lexicon while raising a child with ADHD is critical. It is crucial to remember that each child is unique, and it may take some time to discover the ideal combination of tactics for your child. Above everything, be patient, persistent, and supportive.

It is essential to investigate all possibilities and choose what is best for the kid and family. We'll discuss the benefits of music therapy and how it has aided in the treatment of ADHD in one youngster. We'll also discuss the significance of lifestyle adjustments including nutrition, sleep, and exercise. You may help your child acquire the skills he or she needs to succeed in school, at home, and in life if you take the correct approach.

KNOWING YOUR CHILD'S "EXECUTIVE AGE"

Executive age is a word that relates to a child's brain-developmental stage in terms of self-regulation and executive function. These are the cognitive processes that enable people to plan, organize, begin, and complete tasks. Executive age differs from chronological age and is frequently used to better understand children with ADHD.

It is important to note that children with ADHD may have an executive age that differs from their chronological age. ADHD children and adults, regardless of IQ, are 30% behind in their executive age (Drechsler et al., 2020). This means that a youngster with ADHD who is 10 years old may have the executive age of a seven-year-old.

This is critical for parents to grasp because it can help them better comprehend the difficulties their kid is experiencing. Knowing a kid's executive age can also help parents build more effective symptom management measures for their child. Parents may also wish to pursue treatment or counseling that focuses on executive function abilities, such as cognitive-behavioral therapy or occupational therapy.

MASTER THE "REWARD SYSTEM"

A reward system is a parenting method that uses positive reinforcement to inspire children to perform desired behaviors such as completing chores and following rules. The idea is simple: every time a youngster exhibits a desired behavior, they are rewarded with praise or tiny snacks. A reward system can assist parents of preteens with ADHD in keeping their child engaged and completing assignments.

Children with ADHD frequently have difficulty focusing and controlling their impulses, making it hard for them to finish activities or follow directions. A reward system gives them concrete motivation to stay on course and regulate their desires. Furthermore, using a reward system can boost a child's self-esteem and confidence. When children feel successful and are commended for their positive conduct, they feel valued and loved, which helps to counteract negative feelings linked with ADHD, such as frustration and poor self-worth.

Why it Works

One of the primary reasons why a reward system works for parenting ADHD children is that it aids in the establishment of clear behavioral expectations and boundaries. Children with ADHD frequently experience impulsivity and inattention, making it challenging for them to grasp and follow rules and norms. A reward system helps young children by providing structure and consistency, making it simpler for them to comprehend what is expected of them and focus on the work at hand.

Here are a few clear-cut reasons as to why a reward system is so effective:

- gives children a clear and measurable objective to strive for
- encourages children to concentrate on good habits and actions
- aids children in understanding the relationship between their actions and the consequences
- allows children to see their behavioral development and improvement
- can be tailored to kids' specific requirements and preferences, gives the youngster a feeling of success and self-esteem, and improves parent-child communication and relationships

- provides a more effective and beneficial alternative to punishment-based disciplinary systems
- allows for adaptation and flexibility in dealing with various behaviors and situations

Another reason why a reward system works for ADHD adolescents is because it boosts motivation and engagement. Children with ADHD sometimes suffer from poor motivation, making it difficult for them to finish assignments or participate in activities. Reward systems give these children a feeling of achievement and purpose, which helps to boost their engagement and motivation.

How to Set Up a Reward System

A reward system is an effective tool for parents of preteens with ADHD in managing their child's behavior and motivating them to accomplish chores. Parents may offer their child a sense of success and help them focus on their objectives by instituting a reward system.

Here are some tips for setting up a reward system that will work for your child.

- **Be specific:** Define specific and attainable goals for your child. Instead of asking them to clean their room, for instance, you can ask them to put away their toys or make their bed. This specificity can make it easier for your child to understand what is expected of them and to feel a sense of accomplishment when they meet their goals.

- **Start small:** Begin with simple tasks that your child can accomplish with ease and speed. This helps to build their confidence and momentum as they work toward more challenging tasks. Additionally, starting with small tasks can make it easier for your child to see progress and feel successful.

- **Use positive reinforcement:** Reinforce your child's accomplishments rather than punishing them for their mistakes. This helps to foster a positive outlook and encourages motivation to continue working toward their goals. Encouraging and celebrating successes can have a long-lasting impact on your child's self-esteem and confidence.

- **Be consistent:** Consistently stick to the reward system and give rewards in a timely manner. This helps your child understand that their hard work is being acknowledged and appreciated. Consistency can also help build trust and encourage your child to continue working toward their goals.

- **Make it fun:** Make the reward system an enjoyable and engaging experience for your child. For example, you could create a chart that they can fill out with stickers or use a token system where they can earn points for completing tasks. Making it a fun and exciting experience can help keep your child engaged and motivated.

- **Be flexible:** Be open to adjusting the reward system as needed. If it's not working, try a different approach or set different goals. Flexibility helps to ensure that the reward system remains effective and continues to meet your child's needs as they grow and develop.

- **Get creative:** Get imaginative when setting up the reward system. You could use a jar filled with treats that they can earn or a scavenger hunt that leads to their reward. Creativity can add excitement and intrigue to the reward system, making it more engaging and enjoyable for your child.

- **Be realistic:** Don't set the bar too high. Allow for progress and set achievable goals for your child. Realistic goals can help your child feel successful and motivated, while setting the bar too high can lead to frustration and discouragement.

- **Involve your child:** Engage your child in the process of setting up the reward system. This gives them a sense of ownership and responsibility, and they will be more likely to follow through. Additionally, involving your child in the setup process can help to increase their buy-in and commitment to the system.

- **Celebrate success:** Remember to celebrate and acknowledge your child's progress and success. This helps to communicate to your child that their hard work is being recognized and appreciated, and it encourages them to continue working toward their goals. Celebrating success can also foster a positive outlook and provide a boost of confidence for your child.

Parents may help their child develop confidence, attention, and motivation by establishing a reward system that is explicit, positive, entertaining, consistent, and adaptable. Parents may assist their child in realizing their full potential by being innovative, involving their child, being realistic, and praising accomplishment. Keep in mind that this is a continual process that needs regular monitoring and correction.

Rewards That Work

As a parent of an ADHD preteen, it's critical to discover effective rewards for encouraging your kid to fulfill objectives and improve their behavior. The following incentives have been demonstrated to be very effective for children with ADHD.

- **Fun activities:** A pleasant activity, like playing a game or going to the park, may be a fantastic reward for excellent conduct. This can assist with improving the child's drive to work toward earning the reward while also allowing them to have some fun and let off some steam.
- **Time with parents:** Quality time with parents is also an important reward. This can include going out for a special outing or activity together, or simply spending time together at home.
- **Screen time:** For many children, the opportunity to spend time on a device or watch their favorite TV show can be a powerful reward. You can use this as a reward by setting a goal for your child to reach, and once they

achieve it, they can have a certain amount of screen time.

- **Time with friends:** Social interaction is important for children, and the opportunity to spend time with friends can be a valuable reward. This can include inviting a friend over for a playdate or allowing your child to attend a social event.

- **Their choice:** Giving your child the opportunity to choose their own reward can be a powerful motivator. This can include allowing them to pick out a toy or book or choose a fun activity.

- **Cash:** Earning money may be a great incentive for some youngsters. This may be as basic as rewarding your child with money for completing a chore or meeting a goal.

- **Positive reinforcement:** Positive reinforcement is the practice of rewarding desired behavior with verbal praise, physical touch, or a token reward. This helps to build self-esteem and encourage children to continue to exhibit positive behavior.

- **A sweet treat:** A small treat, like a piece of candy or a cookie, can be a simple but effective reward for a child. This can be especially useful for younger children who may not fully understand the concept of earning a reward.

- **Hugs:** A simple hug or a compliment can be a powerful reward for a child. This physical touch can help to build a positive relationship with your child and also help them to feel safe and loved.

WORK WITH YOUR CHILD'S TEACHERS

Working with their teachers to give support and under-standing is part of parenting a kid with ADHD. This can help identify areas where the youngster is suffering and provide solutions. Teachers might provide concessions such as extra time or the use of fidget toys to help children focus and do well in class. It is also critical to communicate with the teacher about any treatment or medicine that the kid is receiving.

Parents may assist in establishing a conducive learning envi-ronment for their children by actively participating in their education. When dealing with teachers, it is critical to keep an open mind and a readiness to engage. Creating a pleasant home environment that includes a schedule, adequate sleep and exer-cise, and positive reinforcement, may also aid in the management of ADHD symptoms and encourage positive conduct and excellent grades.

Tips to Build a Strong Relationship With Their Teachers

As a parent of a preteen with ADHD, developing close relationships with your child's teachers is critical to ensuring their academic success. Here are some pointers to help you form and maintain a pleasant and productive relationship with your child's instructors.

- **Maintain frequent communication:** Regular contact with your child's teacher is essential for keeping you up to date on your child's academic development and any challenges they may be experiencing. Make an attempt to communicate with them by email, phone conversations, or in-person meetings.
- **Discuss the best methods and times to communicate:** Determine the preferred means of contact for the instructor and reach out to them in a way that is convenient for them. Email, phone conversations, and in-person encounters are all possibilities.
- **Inform about changes at home:** Inform the teacher of any changes at home that may have an influence on your child's education, such as a big life change, or a tough period, so that they can offer understanding and support.
- **Avoid taking things personally:** Keep in mind that the teacher's objective is to assist your child in succeeding, not to be your particular foe. If you disagree with a

teacher's method or conclusion, try to see things from their point of view.

- **Be receptive to suggestions:** Your child's teacher has a wealth of knowledge and may have suggestions that can assist your child. You may collaborate to uncover the finest tactics for your child's achievement if you are receptive to their recommendations.
- **Collaborate on new approaches:** Develop a close relationship with your kid's instructor by experimenting with new things together, such as alternate homework ideas or methods to help your child stay focused. This can lead to the discovery of the most effective strategies for your child's achievement.

THE GENERAL DOS AND THE DON'TS

As a parent of a kid with ADHD, navigating the everyday issues that come with it may be stressful and tough. However, keep in mind that there are things you can do to help your child grow, as well as things you should avoid doing. This section will go over the dos and don'ts of parenting an ADHD child.

✛ *The Dos*

- **Shift your mindset:** It is critical to adjust your perspective from viewing your child's ADHD as a problem to viewing it as a distinct feature of their personality. Instead of focusing on the bad parts, try to focus on your child's talents and positive attributes. This can assist you in approaching parenting in a more positive and helpful manner.
- **Coach and collaborate:** Work with your child's teachers and other professionals to come up with a plan to support your child's needs. Collaboration is key to helping your child succeed in school and other areas of life.
- **Learn and be compassionate:** Learn about ADHD and the unique difficulties that your kid may experience. This will allow you to better understand and sympathize with your child. It is also crucial to be empathetic and patient with your kid, since their symptoms may cause them to feel irritated or overwhelmed.

- **Look for opportunities:** Look for opportunities to help your child build their confidence and skills. Encourage them to take part in activities that they enjoy and that align with their strengths.
- **Determine what good and bad behaviors are:** It is important to have clear rules and boundaries for your child, as this can help to reduce confusion and frustration. Decide ahead of time which behaviors are acceptable and which are not, and make sure your child understands the rules.
- **Celebrate wins:** It is important to celebrate your child's successes, no matter how small they may be. This can help to boost their self-esteem and give them a sense of accomplishment.
- **Define the rules but allow some flexibility:** While it is important to have rules, it is also important to be flexible. Sometimes, your child may struggle to follow the rules and in these cases, it is important to be understanding and to provide guidance and support.

— *The Don'ts*

- **Don't sweat the small stuff:** Try not to get bogged down by small setbacks or challenges. Instead, focus on the bigger picture and remember that progress takes time.
- **Don't think too far ahead:** It can be easy to get caught up in worrying about the future, but it is important to focus on the present and take things one day at a time.

- **Don't be negative:** Avoid speaking negatively about your child or their disorder. This can damage their self-esteem and make it more difficult for them to succeed.
- **Don't let your child or the disorder take control:** While it is important to be understanding and compassionate, it is also important to set boundaries and to be in control of the situation.
- **Don't get overwhelmed and lash out:** Parenting a child with ADHD can be stressful, but it is important to remember that lashing out at your child will not help the situation. Take a step back and try to remain calm and composed.
- **Don't ask too much from your kid:** Be realistic about what your child is capable of and avoid setting unrealistic expectations. Remember that your child is still learning and growing, and it is important to be patient and understanding.

Case Study: Michael Phelps

Michael Phelps is a well-known Olympic champion with a record-breaking 23 gold and 3 silver medals. Despite being diagnosed with ADHD in his childhood, he used his condition to his advantage and went on to become a successful athlete. His mother Debbie played a crucial role in his success by providing him with the necessary support and guidance. She worked closely with Michael's school and helped him focus during competitions by using hand signals to remind him to compose himself.

Michael's story serves as inspiration for parents of children with ADHD, demonstrating that with the right support, children with ADHD can accomplish great things. It also highlights the importance of collaboration between parents and teachers, as well as the development of self-discipline. Debbie's role as a supportive and involved parent shows how important a parent's role can be in helping their child with ADHD.

Furthermore, Michael's story serves as a reminder that ADHD can be channeled into something positive. He used his diagnosis as motivation to achieve his goals and become one of the greatest athletes in history. He is a testament to the fact that children with ADHD have the potential to succeed when they are given the proper support and guidance. Michael Phelps's story is a positive example of how ADHD can be a blessing in disguise.

Activity: Creating a Behavior Chart

Creating a behavior chart can be a helpful tool for parents of children with ADHD. It can provide a visual representation of their child's progress and help them identify patterns in their behavior.

Here are some age-appropriate steps to creating a behavior chart for your preteen with ADHD.

1. **Identify the specific behaviors you want to target:** These can be things like staying on task, completing homework, or managing anger.
2. **Make it interesting:** Create a chart that is visually appealing and age-appropriate for your child. This can

be a simple chart with pictures or a more complex chart with multiple sections.

3. **Decide on a reward system:** This could be something like earning a certain number of stickers to exchange for a prize or privilege.

4. **Be realistic:** Set clear and achievable goals for your child. For example, if the goal is to complete homework on time, set a specific deadline for when it should be finished.

5. **Be consistent:** Use the chart consistently and review it with your child regularly. This will help them see their progress and understand how their behavior affects their rewards.

6. **Be flexible and adjust the chart as needed:** For example, if your child is consistently meeting their goals, you may want to increase the difficulty or set new goals.

If you follow these steps and work closely with your child, a behavior chart can be a valuable tool in managing their ADHD and helping them reach their full potential. It's also important to keep in mind that every child is different and the chart that works for one child may not work for another, so, be open to tweaking and experimenting to find what works best for your child. Remember, it's not about perfection, it's about progress.

4

DEVELOPING HEALTHY HABITS

A s a parent of a preteen with ADHD, you are likely always on the lookout for ways to support your child's health and well-being. Two areas that may be of particular concern are hygiene and healthy habits. Recent studies have shown that children with ADHD may be more prone to bowel problems (Lynn, 2018).

We will cover a range of topics, from teaching your child about the importance of proper hygiene, to strategies for encouraging healthy eating and regular exercise. We will also discuss ways to help your child manage stress and anxiety, which can be particularly challenging for preteens with ADHD. The goal is for you to take an active role in helping your child develop healthy habits that will serve them well throughout their lives.

ENCOURAGE PHYSICAL ACTIVITIES AND TIME OUTDOORS

Physical activity and exposure to nature can have positive effects on children with ADHD. Studies have demonstrated that regular physical exercise can enhance focus and improve the behavior and overall well-being of kids with ADHD (Mehren et al., 2020). Spending time in nature has also been known to reduce hyperactivity and impulsivity. As a parent of an ADHD preteen, promoting physical activity and outdoor time can help you support your child's general health and well-being.

This can also provide an opportunity for your child to improve self-discipline, social skills, and self-esteem. Additionally, participating in physical activity can improve sleep (which is often disrupted in children with ADHD) and boost healthy habits, overall. Encouraging your preteen to engage in physical activities like team sports, swimming, or hiking can not only mitigate ADHD symptoms but it can also foster a healthy lifestyle. Hence, this is a beneficial situation for both the parent and child.

How Exercise Helps Kids With ADHD

As a parent of a preteen with ADHD, it's critical to understand the advantages of exercise for your child. Exercise has been found in studies to be an effective strategy to reduce ADHD symptoms such as impulsivity and hyperactivity. Indeed, studies have shown that regular physical exercise is just as helpful as medicine in lowering ADHD symptoms in youngsters.

Exercise for ADHD preteens:

- improves general physical health and fitness
- enhances concentration and focus
- improves impulse control and hyperactivity
- increases self-esteem and self-worth
- improves sleep quality
- reduces anxiety and depression symptoms
- improves stress tolerance
- enhances memory and cognitive performance by increasing brain chemicals associated with attention and focus
- improves social connections and talents

When it comes to the amount of physical exercise suggested for children with ADHD, the American Academy of Pediatrics (2022) suggests that children and adolescents obtain at least 60 minutes of moderate to vigorous physical activity every day. Running, swimming, cycling, and sports are examples of such activities.

It is critical to emphasize that the sort of exercise is less significant than the fact that the youngster is moving. A youngster with ADHD may struggle to concentrate during activities that involve a lot of sitting or silence such as yoga or tai chi. Martial arts and dance, on the other hand, can be excellent choices since they mix movement with structure and discipline.

Best Types of Activities for Them

Physical activity is a great way for kids with ADHD to release energy and improve focus.

- **Encourage outdoor activities:** Parents can help their kids get outside and stay active by participating in outdoor activities such as hiking, biking, and running.
- **Join team sports for camaraderie:** Team sports like soccer, basketball, and baseball are beneficial for kids with ADHD because they offer structure and a sense of community. Consider signing your child up for a local youth league or after-school program.
- **Focus through individual sports:** Individual sports like swimming, martial arts, and gymnastics are great for kids with ADHD as they provide a sense of

accomplishment and an opportunity to set and achieve personal goals.

- **Play active games for fun:** Active games such as tag, capture the flag, or Simon says are great ways for kids to release energy and have fun. These games can be played at a park or in your own backyard.
- **Improve focus with dance:** Dancing can be a fun way for kids with ADHD to release energy and improve focus. Parents can enroll their child in a local dance class or put some music on and dance with their child at home.

Keep in mind that each child is unique and may have different preferences for physical activities. Parents should try a variety of activities with their child to see which ones they enjoy the most. Encourage your child to try new things and pursue their interests. With the right activities and support, children with ADHD can live busy and healthy lives.

Tips to Get Them Moving Daily

- **Start small by doing 30 minutes a day:** Encourage your child to engage in physical activity, even if it's just for a short time. You can suggest taking a walk around the block, doing a quick workout video, or anything that gets them moving.
- **A balanced workout:** To keep your child engaged and healthy, it's important to include a variety of exercises in their routine, such as cardio and strength training.

- **Consistency is key:** Regular exercise is more beneficial than intense workouts done infrequently. Encourage your child to engage in physical activity every day, even if it's only for a few minutes.
- **Any movement counts:** The focus should be on getting your child active, regardless of the type of exercise they do. Dancing to music, playing tag, or any other fun activity can be just as effective.
- **Join a sport:** Joining a sports team or club can be a great way for kids with ADHD to stay active and learn important skills such as teamwork and discipline.
- **Exercise solo or with a group:** Some kids may prefer to exercise alone, while others may enjoy working out with others. Choose activities that suit your child's preferences.
- **Mix it up:** Keep things interesting by switching up your child's exercise routine, trying new activities, or changing the time and location of their workouts. This can help maintain their motivation and engagement.
- **Enjoy the great outdoors:** Encourage your child to get outside and enjoy nature. Activities like hiking, biking, or playing at the park can provide a source of inspiration and motivation to stay active.

TEACH THEM HOW TO EAT RIGHT

As a parent of an ADHD preteen, it's important to understand the relationship between food and ADHD symptoms. Studies have shown that certain foods and nutrients can have an impact on ADHD symptoms, and maintaining healthy eating habits can be beneficial for children with ADHD (Castle, 2021).

It's well known that a diet high in sugar, preservatives, and processed foods can exacerbate symptoms of ADHD. On the other hand, a diet rich in fruit, vegetables, and whole grains can help to improve focus and concentration. Additionally, research has also shown that certain nutrients, such as omega-3 fatty acids and zinc, may be beneficial for children with ADHD (Resnick, 2022).

It's important to note that there is no one specific "ADHD diet" that works for every child. However, by promoting healthy eating habits and providing your child with a balanced diet, you can help to minimize symptoms and improve overall health.

Why the Right Diet Matters

A healthy diet is important for all children, but it is especially important for preteens with ADHD. Certain foods have been shown in studies to aggravate ADHD symptoms, while others have been shown to improve them (Roybal, 2008). For example, a diet that is high in sugar, artificial colors, and preservatives can aggravate symptoms, whereas a diet that is high in fruit, vegetables, and omega-3 fatty acids can improve them.

The Feingold Diet, which eliminates artificial colors, preservatives, and other synthetic ingredients, is one of the most effective diets for ADHD. This diet has been shown to help with symptoms like hyperactivity, impulsivity, and inattention (Bernstein, 2022). The Mediterranean diet, which emphasizes fruit, vegetables, whole grains, and healthy fats, has also been found to be beneficial, especially in relation to mental health (Darabi et al., 2021).

It's critical to remember that each child with ADHD is unique, and what works for one may not work for another. Working with a professional, registered dietitian can assist you in developing a diet that is tailored to your child's specific needs.

Eat More of These

A diet that is rich in fruits, vegetables, and omega-3 fatty acids can improve ADHD symptoms, while a diet high in sugar, artificial colors, and preservatives can worsen them. These are some essential nutrients you can include in your preteen's diet to ensure they are meeting their dietary needs.

1. **Protein:** Foods rich in protein, such as lean meat, fish, eggs, beans, and nuts, are essential for preteens with ADHD as they help to stabilize blood sugar levels and promote focus and concentration. Protein also helps to build and repair tissues, making it a vital nutrient for overall growth and development.
2. **Complex carbohydrates:** Complex carbohydrates, such as whole grains, fruits, and vegetables, provide preteens with a steady supply of energy throughout the day. These foods are also high in fiber, which helps to regulate digestion and promote feelings of fullness. Complex carbohydrates are also a good source of

vitamins and minerals, which are essential for overall health and well-being.

3. **Omega-3 fatty acids:** Omega-3 fatty acids are essential fatty acids that are found in fish (such as salmon) and in certain types of nuts and seeds. These fatty acids are important for brain health and have been shown to improve focus, concentration, and overall cognitive function in preteens with ADHD. They also have anti-inflammatory properties, which can help to reduce symptoms of ADHD and other conditions.

It's important to work with a professional, such as a registered dietitian, to help you create a diet that is tailored to your child's specific needs and to help you stick to it. It's easy to want to give in to your child's cravings and let them eat whatever they want, but in the long run, sticking to a healthy diet will be beneficial for them.

What to Avoid

When it comes to the diet of a child with ADHD, it is important to be aware of certain foods that should be avoided in order to help manage their symptoms.

1. **Refined and simple carbohydrates:** These types of carbohydrates include white bread, pastries, sugary cereals, and other processed foods. These foods can cause a spike in blood sugar levels which can lead to hyperactivity and impulsivity in children with ADHD. It's best to avoid these types of foods and opt for whole

grains like quinoa, brown rice, and whole wheat bread instead.

2. **Caffeine:** Caffeine can have a stimulating effect on the brain and can worsen symptoms of ADHD. Common sources of caffeine include soda, energy drinks, and chocolate. Parents should be aware of the caffeine content in their child's food and drink, and limit their intake.

3. **Food additives:** Certain food additives like artificial colors, flavors, and preservatives can also worsen symptoms of ADHD. These additives are often found in processed foods and snack foods. Parents should be mindful of the ingredients in the food they give to their child, and they should avoid any foods that contain artificial additives.

It's important to note that a healthy diet alone may not be enough to alleviate symptoms of ADHD, but it can certainly be a helpful part of a larger treatment plan. It's always best to consult with a health-care professional before making any changes to your child's diet.

Creating Good Eating Habits

Creating good eating habits for children with ADHD is important for managing their symptoms and overall health. The following are some tips for establishing healthy eating habits for preteens with ADHD.

- **Stick to a meal schedule and establish a routine:** When it comes to controlling ADHD symptoms, consistency is essential and this includes meal times. A consistent eating plan can help manage blood sugar levels, which can increase focus and concentration.
- **Stock healthy snacks and avoid fast food restaurants:** Children with ADHD frequently have difficulty sitting still and focusing, so having healthy snacks on hand will help to keep them going throughout the day. Avoiding fast food restaurants can also be beneficial, as these items are frequently high in sugar, fat, and other ingredients that can aggravate ADHD symptoms.
- **Include your child in the process:** Involving your child in the process of developing healthy eating habits can make them feel more invested and motivated to follow through on the plan. Encourage them to assist in meal planning, grocery shopping, and food preparation.
- **Encourage experimentation:** Allowing children with ADHD to experiment with different ingredients and recipes may encourage them to try new foods. Don't be disheartened if they don't like new foods at first, keep trying and find something that they will enjoy.
- **Be persistent:** Changing one's eating habits might be challenging, so it's critical to persevere and not give up. It may take some time for your child to acclimate to new foods and eating habits, but with patience and perseverance, they will get there.
- **Avoid dramatic dietary changes:** Making drastic dietary changes for your child might be daunting and difficult to adjust to. Instead, make minor changes

gradually over time to make things easier for your youngster.

- **Find visually appealing and fun-to-eat foods:** Because some children with ADHD may be picky eaters, it's critical to find foods that are aesthetically appealing and entertaining to eat. To make food more fascinating and appealing to your child, experiment with different colors and shapes.

Creating healthy eating habits for children with ADHD is an ongoing process that requires patience, persistence, and a willingness to experiment. By following these tips, parents can help their children manage their symptoms and improve their overall health and well-being.

INSTILL GOOD SLEEPING HABITS

Adequate sleep is crucial for children with ADHD as it helps improve their attention, behavior, and overall well-being. However, many children with ADHD struggle with insomnia or other sleep disorders that can further exacerbate their symptoms. Therefore, it is essential for parents to instill good sleeping habits in their children with ADHD.

One of the common side effects of ADHD is difficulty sleeping. Studies have shown that children and teens with ADHD are more likely to have sleep problems than those without the condition (Villines, 2021). They may have difficulty falling asleep and staying asleep, or they may have restless sleep. This can lead to fatigue and irritability during the day, which can further exacerbate symptoms of ADHD.

Effects of ADHD on sleep:

- difficulty falling asleep
- difficulty staying asleep
- restless sleep
- fatigue
- irritability

There are several reasons why ADHD affects sleep. Children with ADHD may have trouble settling down at bedtime because their brains are still active. They may also have difficulty staying asleep due to the impulsivity and hyperactivity associated with ADHD. Additionally, some children with ADHD take medication that can affect their sleep patterns.

How to Ensure Good Quality Sleep

- **Make sleep a priority:** Establishing good sleeping habits can help children with ADHD get the rest they need to function at their best. This includes creating a healthy sleeping environment, implementing sleep hygiene, and sticking to a bedtime routine.
- **Start tasks early:** Children with ADHD may struggle with focusing and completing tasks, so starting homework and responsibilities as soon as possible in the evening can help ensure they are finished before bed.
- **Limit screen time:** The blue light emitted from electronic devices can interfere with the body's production of melatonin, a hormone that regulates sleep. Limiting or eliminating screen time close to bedtime can help ensure the brain produces enough melatonin for a good night's sleep.
- **Try white noise:** Children with ADHD may be more sensitive to noise and find it hard to fall asleep in a quiet environment. Using white noise apps or noise machines can help muffle background noise and create a peaceful sleep environment.
- **Address needs:** To help children with ADHD transition from being active to winding down for bed, it's important to address any needs such as hunger or thirst before bedtime.
- **Create a comfortable sleeping environment:** To promote better sleep, parents can create a cool, dark,

quiet bedroom and invest in comfortable mattresses
and pillows.

- **Practice good sleep hygiene:** Good sleep hygiene
  includes habits like avoiding caffeine and heavy meals
  close to bedtime, avoiding napping during the day, and
  establishing a relaxing bedtime routine.

SUCCEED AT POTTY TRAINING

Due to their impulsiveness and trouble with attention and
focus, potty training can be a difficult milestone for preteens
with ADHD. They can, however, develop this vital ability with
the correct help and tactics. Potty training can take longer for
children with ADHD, and parents should be aware of any
sensory sensitivities their child may have.

Sensory sensitivities can benefit from accommodations such as
a flushing sound machine. Potty training is essential for children with ADHD because it promotes independence, self-regulation, and self-esteem. Parents with ADHD can assist their
child with ADHD in completing this essential phase with
patience and suitable tactics.

- **Stick to a consistent schedule:** A consistent potty-
  training routine can help youngsters with ADHD to
  stay on track and remember when it is time to use the
  restroom. This can include taking toilet breaks
  throughout the day and setting alarms to remind your
  child to go.

- **Use visual cues:** Visual cues, such as charts or stickers, can be beneficial for ADHD youngsters because they provide a clear and real way to track progress. Parents can make a chart with images of their children using the restroom and reward them with stickers or other items for successful trips to the toilet.
- **Break it down into small steps:** Potty training may be stressful for children with ADHD, but breaking it down into tiny, manageable steps can help make the process less stressful. Starting with just sitting on the toilet and gradually progressing to using it for pee and bowel movements is one option.
- **Use positive reinforcement:** Positive reinforcement, such as verbal praise, prizes, or little snacks, can help motivate children with ADHD to stick to their potty-training schedules. Positive reinforcement and rewards for even minor accomplishments should be provided by parents.
- **Be patient and consistent:** Potty training may be a lengthy and challenging process, particularly for children with ADHD. Parents must be patient and consistent in their efforts, and they must not become discouraged if there are setbacks or accidents. It's also crucial to remember that each child is unique, and potty training may take longer for some.

MAINTAIN OVERALL GOOD PERSONAL HYGIENE

Children with ADHD may struggle with executive functioning skills, making it difficult for them to remember to practice good hygiene. They may also have difficulty paying attention to detail and completing tasks, making it hard for them to complete all of the steps of regular personal hygiene chores. Children with ADHD may be less likely to halt and contemplate the consequences of poor hygiene (such as the risk of illness or social rejection) due to their impulsivity.

These are a few areas that are specifically affected.

- **Oral hygiene:** Children with ADHD may forget to brush their teeth, floss, or use mouthwash. They may also have trouble with fine motor skills, making it difficult for them to properly clean their teeth and gums. A child with ADHD may also have trouble sitting still long enough to brush their teeth for the recommended two minutes.
- **Body hygiene:** Children with ADHD may not want to take showers or baths regularly. They may also have trouble with fine motor skills, making it difficult for them to properly wash and clean themselves. A child with ADHD may also have trouble sitting still long enough to complete a shower or bath.
- **Washing hands:** Children with ADHD may forget to wash their hands before meals or after using the bathroom. They may also have trouble with fine motor skills, making it difficult for them to properly wash their hands and clean under their nails. A child with ADHD may also have trouble holding still long enough to wash their hands for the recommended 20 seconds.

Case Study: Good Hygiene

Lacey and Jack

Lacey's child, Jack, was diagnosed with ADHD at a young age and she faced challenges in finding activities that could keep him engaged and healthy. Lacey tried various options, from sports to art classes, but nothing seemed to work. One day, while walking in their neighborhood, Lacey and Jack came across a community garden. Jack was fascinated by the colorful flowers and the various types of vegetables growing there. Lacey saw the interest in Jack's eyes and decided to explore this further.

The following day, Lacey enrolled Jack in a gardening class at the community garden. He learned how to plant and care for different veggies, as well as the benefits of eating fresh fruits and vegetables. Jack enjoyed being outdoors and learning about the different types of plants and their growth cycles. He also loved the physical activity involved in digging and planting.

Lacey noticed a significant change in Jack's behavior and energy levels. He was more focused, calm, and would come home from school excited to work on his garden. He even started experimenting with different gardening techniques and was thrilled when he was able to harvest his own vegetables.

Lacey was pleased to see her son's interest in an activity that was not only enjoyable but also helped him stay active and healthy. She realized that the key was to find activities that were tailored to Jack's interests and energy levels. From then on, Lacey made sure to provide Jack with more outdoor activities that kept him engaged and healthy.

Rhadia and Ahmed

Rhadia had difficulty getting her son Ahmed to practice good hygiene, as he had been diagnosed with ADHD and sensory issues and resisted brushing his teeth, taking showers, and washing his hands. She stumbled upon an article detailing strategies to help children with these conditions maintain good hygiene, and decided to put these tips into practice. She created a schedule and posted it on the fridge, along with reminders throughout the day.

To make brushing his teeth more enjoyable, she bought Ahmed a timer toothbrush and let him choose his own toothpaste flavor. She allowed him to select his own soap, shampoo, and conditioner for showers, and kept the water temperature comfortable and under his control. To encourage hand washing, Rhadia provided a fun soap dispenser and let Ahmed sing his favorite song while washing. These strategies were successful and helped Ahmed practice good hygiene, leading to improved health and happiness for both him and Rhadia. She was grateful for the information she found in the article and pleased with the improved results.

Activity: At Home Workout

Exercise is a crucial part of maintaining a healthy lifestyle for children with ADHD, and it can be challenging to find activities that will keep them engaged and motivated. Here are some easy and fun indoor exercise ideas that you can try right now at home.

1. **Obstacle course:** Set up a course using household items like pillows, chairs, and boxes. Children can jump, crawl, and climb through the course. You can even make it a competition to see who can complete it the fastest.
2. **Yoga:** Yoga is a great way to improve flexibility and balance. There are many kid-friendly yoga videos available online that parents can follow along with their child.
3. **Dance party:** Put on some upbeat music and have a dance party in the living room. Dancing is a fun way to get moving and burn off energy.
4. **Hula-hoop:** Hula-hooping is a fun way to improve coordination and core strength. Parents can even join in the fun and have a hula-hooping competition.
5. **Balloon volleyball:** Blow up a balloon and use it to play a game of volleyball. This is a great way to improve hand-eye coordination and burn off energy.
6. **Jump rope:** Jumping rope is a great cardiovascular workout. If a traditional jump rope is too difficult, parents can try using a piece of fabric or a scarf.

These are just a few ideas for indoor exercises that you can try with your preteen. The most important thing is to make it fun and interactive for the child. Encourage them to try different exercises and find something that they enjoy. Give it a try as soon as you can.

THE VALUE OF A BREAK

"In this game, everyone needs a break to refuel, recharge, and jump back to full throttle."

— HELEN EDWARDS

You're soaking up a lot of information here, and it's about time to take a pause. Breaks are good for all of us, and they're something your child will need to learn to use as they progress through adolescence and into adulthood.

The key for them will be in learning the difference between a 'good break' (one that has a clear time frame, allows them to rest, and enables them to return to the task at hand easily) and a 'bad break' (one that has no clear cut-off point and sends them down a rabbit hole of related activities).

But for you right now, just a short break to reflect on the information you're learning and how you can use it to help you is all you need.

As you're all too aware, parenting a child with ADHD can feel overwhelming and isolating, and hopefully, by this stage in the book, you're starting to see some ways you can make your experience – and that of your child – a little easier.

You also have a unique opportunity to help another parent in your situation – without doing anything more than writing a few sentences.

By leaving a review of this book on Amazon, you'll show other parents not only that they're not alone, but exactly where they can find the guidance they need as their child approaches adolescence.

Simply by letting other readers know how this book has helped you and what they'll find inside, you can help other parents along this difficult journey and steer them towards the resources they need to make it easier.

Thank you for your support. Children with ADHD need our guidance – but we need guidance too if we're to help them effectively.

5

IMPROVING SOCIAL SKILLS

A DHD can be a significant difficulty for youngsters, particularly when it comes to social skills. Children with ADHD may struggle to make and keep friends, leading to feelings of isolation and low self-esteem. However, it is critical to remember that these social issues are caused by ADHD symptoms rather than a lack of desire for friends.

According to current research, more than half of children with ADHD do not have reciprocating friendships, and more than 75% of children with ADHD and behavioral issues do not have friends in their classroom (Start Here Parents, 2020). These data demonstrate the difficulties that children with ADHD encounter in developing and maintaining friendships. Furthermore, research indicates that the quality of friendships formed by children with ADHD is frequently inadequate, with frequent disagreement and a lack of emotional connection (Mrug et al., 2012).

HOW ADHD AFFECTS ONE'S SOCIAL COMPETENCE

Social competence is a broad collection of talents that are necessary for efficient social interaction. Good social skills can assist neurotypical youngsters in developing strong relationships with peers, maintaining those ties over time, and responding properly to social cues and situations. Children with ADHD, on the other hand, may find it substantially more challenging to fulfill these objectives.

There are various reasons why children with ADHD may struggle with their social skills. First, they may not be able to pay attention and commit things to memory as easily as expected. Their executive functioning might be a impaired, making it a struggle to plan and organize social interactions.

Impulsivity can also make it difficult for children with ADHD to regulate their emotions, control their conduct, and respond properly to social cues and circumstances. For example, they are prone to acting rashly, speaking before thinking, and being too emotional in social situations.

Finally, children with ADHD may struggle with social perception and interpretation, making it challenging for them to comprehend and respond to social cues and circumstances. They may, for example, struggle to recognize nonverbal signs such as body language, tone of voice, and facial expressions. This might make it difficult for them to read the emotions and ideas of others, leading to misunderstandings and social gaffes.

Common Social Challenges

ADHD is well-known for making life difficult in a variety of ways, including when it comes to developing social skills. Many children with ADHD have difficulty making and maintaining friendships, conversing, and understanding social cues. As a parent, you must understand these common social challenges and how to assist your child in overcoming them.

These are the most common social challenges that children with ADHD face.

1. **Trouble picking up on social cues:** Children with ADHD may have difficulty reading body language, tone of voice, and other nonverbal cues. This can lead to misunderstandings and difficulties in social situations.
2. **Trouble keeping friends:** Children with ADHD may struggle to maintain healthy friendships due to impulsiveness, irritability, or forgetfulness.

3. **Going off-topic:** Children with ADHD may struggle to stay focused during conversations, leading them to frequently go off-topic.

4. **Being unreliable:** Children with ADHD may forget important commitments or be late for appointments, making it difficult for them to build and maintain relationships.

5. **Overreacting:** Children with ADHD may have trouble regulating their emotions, leading them to overreact in social situations.

DEVELOPING SOCIAL EXECUTIVE FUNCTION SKILLS

Social executive function skills are critical in a child's capacity to engage with others and develop relationships. They include the ability to recognize and control one's emotions and conduct, as well as respond correctly to social cues. These abilities enable neurotypical children to easily navigate social interactions and form meaningful connections with others. However, developing these social executive function skills in children with ADHD might be difficult.

There are a few things that parents may do to help their preteen with ADHD to develop these important social executive function skills. By implementing these tactics, you can help your preteen lay the groundwork for successful social interactions and lasting connections in their future relationships.

1. **Model perspective-taking by sharing your internal dialogue:** Encourage your child to understand and empathize with others by sharing your thoughts and feelings. By doing so, you are teaching them how to think from someone else's point of view, which is essential in social situations where it's crucial to understand and react to others' emotions and thoughts.

2. **Emphasize the importance of "fake-outs" for impulse control:** Children with ADHD may have trouble controlling impulses and may act without thinking. By educating them about "fake-outs," you are teaching them the value of pausing and considering their actions before reacting. For instance, if someone makes a face or says something that might come across as rude, explain that it may not be intentional, encourage them to be more tolerant and avoid aggressive reactions.

3. **Encourage efforts with positive reinforcement:** Boost your child's self-esteem and confidence by positively reinforcing their efforts in social situations. When you observe your child making an effort, praise them and motivate them to continue working on their social skills.

4. **Assist in understanding the context:** Children with ADHD may have trouble comprehending the context of a social situation, which can lead to misunderstandings and inappropriate behavior. Help them by explaining the rules and expectations of social settings such as restaurants or schools.

5. **Practice situational awareness together:** Improve your child's ability to understand and react to others'

emotions, thoughts, and behavior in social situations by practicing "reading the field" together. For example, point out when someone is sad or upset and talk about how to respond empathetically.

6. **Remind them of past social successes:** Children with ADHD may struggle with short-term memory and forget past social successes. By reminding them of these achievements, you can boost their confidence and encourage them to keep developing their social skills.

7. **Avoid comparing to family interactions:** Children with ADHD may have difficulty with social skills, but they may feel more comfortable and confident with family members. It's important to remember that their social skills with family may not be representative of their abilities in other social settings. By avoiding comparisons, you can help them develop their social skills without adding unnecessary stress.

These tactics can assist youngsters with ADHD in improving their social executive function skills and navigating social situations with greater ease and confidence. It's vital to remember that developing these abilities takes time, and that patience and support are essential for success. Children with ADHD can learn the skills they need to flourish in social situations with the correct help and direction.

MAKING FRIENDS

Making friends is a vital part of growing up since it can help youngsters improve their self-esteem, social skills, and minimize feelings of loneliness. Making friends might be especially difficult for children with ADHD, but it is not impossible. Joining clubs, events, and programs, being polite and sociable, and learning to take turns and share are all general ideas for establishing friendships. Finding friends with similar interests, practicing social skills in therapy, and finding a mentor are advised for preteens with ADHD.

The pre-teen years can be difficult for many children, including those who do not have ADHD. During this stage, children are forming their sense of identity and learning to navigate social relationships. Peer acceptability becomes essential, and many children begin to worry about fitting in and establishing friends.

It is critical for parents to be proactive in assisting their child in finding opportunities to socialize and establish friends. This could include encouraging them to go on playdates with other children, enrolling them in after-school activities, or assisting them in joining a sports team. It is also vital to explain to your child about the importance of friendship and to give them advice on how to make friends. You can encourage them to listen to other people, demonstrate how to show kindness to others, and remind them to focus on shared interests.

Create Opportunities for Friendship Development

As children grow older, they become increasingly self-sufficient and rely less on their parents for social engagement. Children gain crucial life skills such as communication, conflict resolution, and empathy during this stage. It is critical for parents to provide opportunities for friendship formation in order to promote their child's social development and help them establish a strong sense of self.

Here are some ways you can create opportunities for your child to make friends.

- **Join a sports team:** Sports provide a pleasant and supportive environment for youngsters to make friends and develop social skills.
- **Enroll in classes or clubs:** Enrolling in classes or groups that match with your child's interests will allow

him or her to meet new people who share similar interests.

- **Volunteer:** Volunteering allows children to give back to the community while meeting new people and gaining vital social skills.
- **Participate in community activities:** Attending community events such as festivals, fairs, and concerts will allow you to engage with others and create new acquaintances.
- **Invite other children over for playdates:** Inviting other children over to play is a simple and successful way to let your child mingle and establish new friends.
- **Join a youth group:** Youth organizations are an excellent opportunity for children to meet new people while engaging in fun and informative activities.

Role-Playing and Modeling Friendship

Role-playing and modeling friendship are two of the most effective approaches to helping preteens with ADHD acquire social skills. Role-playing is when you act out scenarios with your child to show them how to react in social situations. This allows your child to practice their social skills in a secure, controlled environment while receiving feedback from you. When you model friendship for your child, you act as a friend yourself. This includes being a good listener, displaying empathy, and being respectful.

When role-playing and modeling friendship with your child, consider circumstances that are relevant to your child's life and that they can relate to. You may, for example, role-play how to initiate a discussion with someone, how to make and maintain a promise, or how to resolve a quarrel. By practicing these abilities, your child will learn to feel more confident when confronted with similar situations in real life.

Work With the School to Improve Peer Status

Working with your child's school to improve their peer status is another strategy for creating more opportunities for friendship formation. Reaching out to teachers, guidance counselors, and administrators to discuss your child's social skills and the tactics that have worked best for them might be part of this.

Working with the school to improve peer status can involve several different strategies, including:

- creating social skills groups in which children can practice their social skills in a safe, organized atmosphere
- encouraging your child to participate in group activities and events where they can make new friends and improve social skills, such as sports teams or clubs
- involving your child in school-wide activities such as volunteering or community service initiatives where they can collaborate with other students and form friendships
- encouraging your child to participate in a mentorship program where he or she will work one-on-one with a

peer who has good social skills and can serve as a
positive role model

Working with the school to improve your child's peer status is a
team effort that can benefit your child's social skills and self-
esteem. It is critical to be proactive and to maintain contact
with the school on a frequent basis to ensure that your child has
the necessary help to flourish.

IMPROVING BEHAVIORS

Managing social situations can be difficult for youngsters with
ADHD. The impulsiveness and lack of social awareness that can
accompany ADHD might result in acts that are misconstrued or
misinterpreted by others. These behaviors might range from
interrupting others while they are speaking to having problems
with adhering to social rules and traditions. It is useful for
parents to be aware of these habits and work with their children to improve them.

Impulsiveness is one of the issues that children with ADHD
encounter, it can lead to interrupting others, making inappropriate statements, or acting without thinking. It is critical to
encourage youngsters to pause and reflect before saying or
acting in order to avoid harmful behaviors. This can be accomplished through role-playing exercises, social stories, and other
activities that teach children the importance of pausing to think
before acting.

Another issue that children with ADHD face is trouble
adhering to social norms and practices. This might result in

actions such as disrespecting personal boundaries, neglecting to take turns in discussion, or failing to demonstrate empathy for others. To assist children in improving these behaviors, it is critical to teach them about the social standards and conventions they should adhere to, as well as the repercussions of failing to do so. This can be accomplished through clear and consistent regulations, positive reinforcement, and social stories that teach children the value of adhering to social norms and traditions.

Preventing Bad Behaviors

It might be tough, as a parent of a preteen with ADHD, to manage some behaviors that could be impeding their social skills development. Poor impulse control, striking, and speaking harsh things are all unacceptable habits that should be addressed and eliminated. These activities can endanger others, ruin relationships, and have a detrimental impact on your child's social status.

To help your child stop these behaviors, it is important to address the root cause, which may be related to ADHD or other factors.

- **Poor impulse control**

It is critical to teach a preteen with weak impulse control to think before acting. It can be beneficial to encourage them to pause and contemplate the ramifications of their actions. Encourage them to employ coping methods like counting to 10, deep breathing, or finding a quiet area to relax. Teaching children mindfulness skills to help them regulate their emotions can also be beneficial.

- **Hitting**

Hitting is an inappropriate act that must be addressed quickly. Teach your youngster that physical aggression is never the answer. Establish clear repercussions for hitting, such as time-outs or loss of privileges. There must be consequences for their actions, to help them understand their wrongdoing. Once an act of aggression occurs, it is important to act immediately to correct the behavior. You can use modeling and communication to show the right and wrong ways to express anger or frustration. Positive reinforcement is also important, you should reward your child for expressing their feelings through constructive means like talking, painting, or writing.

- **Saying rude things**

Saying hurtful things can damage relationships; therefore, it's critical to teach preteens the importance of their words. This is directly tied to ADHD, which causes impulsive behavior. It can be beneficial to encourage preteens to consider their words before they speak. Additionally, modeling positive communication skills and praising children when they use respectful language can be beneficial. Teach them empathy and inspire them to imagine themselves in the shoes of others. Role-playing exercises can also help your child practice proper social skills.

It is also important to recognize that altering behavior takes time and patience, and that consistency is valuable when in addressing the behaviors. It's also beneficial to have open and honest dialogue with the adolescent in order to understand the underlying causes of their behavior and collaborate with them on finding solutions.

Nurturing Good Behaviors

To help your adolescent with ADHD build stronger social skills, it is crucial to work on improving other behaviors. Two skills that can be learned to improve social interactions are conflict resolution and turning away from stressors.

1. Resolving Conflict

Conflict resolution is a key social skill for children with ADHD. Parents can assist their child to improve this skill by encouraging them to use constructive communication, actively listen to others' opinions, and accept responsibility for their actions. Parents can also role-play various scenarios with their child to learn to resolve problems in a constructive manner.

Encourage them to seek solutions that are fair and mindful of all parties involved. It is essential to teach youngsters the virtues of compromise and negotiation. Parents can also teach their child to walk away from the situation and calm down before settling the disagreement. Parents can help their children to see the consequences of their words and actions on others.

2. Facing Away From Triggers

Preteens with ADHD are readily aroused by their surroundings, which results in impulsive and reactive behavior. Parents can help their child identify triggers and develop methods to avoid or control them to help improve this. This is a crucial skill to cultivate because it can assist your child in better managing their emotions and behaviors.

If a child is easily aroused by loud noises, for example, parents can advise them to wear noise-canceling headphones or leave the environment. Parents can also teach their children deep breathing and mindfulness practices to help them stay calm and focused in stressful situations. Seek the assistance of a therapist, if necessary, who can assist your child in developing and implementing good coping techniques.

Improving social skills in preteens with ADHD takes time, effort, and consistency. Parents can help their children develop the social skills they need to succeed in life by working with them to stop harmful behaviors and promote positive actions.

DEALING WITH BULLYING

Bullying is a prevalent problem for many preteens, particularly those who are neurodivergent. Children with ADHD are more likely to be bullied because their behavior and social skills make them a target for teasing and mockery. This might have an adverse effect on their self-esteem and mental health.

Bullying in preteens can take numerous forms, including physical violence, verbal abuse, and cyberbullying. To guarantee their child's safety, parents must be aware of various types of bullying and monitor their child's social media activities. In addition to monitoring their child's internet activity, parents should look for indicators of bullying in their child's behavior, such as withdrawal from social activities, falling grades, and unexpected changes in mood or demeanor.

Bullying is a serious problem that affects many preteens, particularly those with ADHD. It is critical for parents to understand the many types of bullying and to watch their child's conduct and internet activities. Parents can help avoid bullying and encourage their child's development of healthy relationships by teaching social skills and coping methods and encouraging open communication.

Here are some strategies you can use to help your child.

1. Provide social cues

This can include instructing students on how to use facial expressions, body language, and tone of voice to convey various emotions and attitudes. You can, for example, try making varied expressions and tones of voice to portray emotions such as happiness, rage, and sadness. You can also teach your youngster about how different social cues affect how others perceive and respond to them.

2. Promote the value of compassion

Promoting the value of compassion is another key step in assisting your child in dealing with teasing and bullying. Children with ADHD may struggle with empathy and understanding others' points of view. Thus, it is critical to assist them to develop compassion and understanding for others. This can include teaching kids about different emotions, what it's like to be in someone else's shoes, and what influence their actions can have on others. You can also inspire kids to be kind and compassionate by performing acts of service, volunteering, or simply being there for those in need.

3. Teach the difference between benign teasing and bullying

Explain to your youngster the differences between teasing and bullying. Teasing can be playful and innocent at times, whereas bullying is malicious and intended to cause harm. You may help your youngster to comprehend this distinction by providing examples and addressing why bullying is harmful. Explain that teasing becomes bullying when it is repeated and intentional, and when it causes pain or discomfort to another person.

4. Teach your child how to spot bullying

Another key step is to teach your youngster how to recognize bullying. You can assist kids in understanding what bullying looks like and what warning signals to watch for. Bullying can include physical aggression, verbal abuse, exclusion, spreading rumors, and internet harassment, for example. You can also talk with your child about what they should do if they notice bullying, such as reporting it to a teacher, sticking up for the victim, or seeking support from a trustworthy adult.

Remember that bullying can have a negative impact on your child's mental health and self-esteem. You can help your child feel confident and safe as they navigate social situations and possibly hazardous interactions by providing these tactics and tools. When it comes to dealing with bullying, it is critical that you as a parent provide your child with the tools and tactics necessary to respond in a safe and effective manner.

Here are some of the ways that your child can respond to bullying.

- **Use humor:** Humor may be an excellent tool for defusing tense circumstances. If your youngster can find a way to make light of the situation, it may take the wind out of the bully's sails. Your child can use comedy to divert attention away from the bullying and redirect it to something else. For example, if the bully makes fun of your child's shoes, your child could respond, "Well, at least I can run faster than you!"

- **Agree with the bully:** Another option is to side with the bully. This might be disarming to the bully and cause the situation to lose strength. For example, if the bully makes fun of your child's height, your youngster could respond, "Yes, I am aware that I am short. But don't worry, I still have a large heart!"

- **Answer back with sarcasm:** When used correctly, sarcasm can be a potent tool. If your youngster is quick on the draw, they can use sarcasm to stun or silence the bully. For example, if a bully mocks your child's clothing, your youngster could respond, "Thanks for noticing, I really wanted to make a fashion statement today."

- **Avoid the bully:** It is acceptable for your youngster to avoid the bully if he or she lacks a swift retort. To prevent additional contact, your youngster might just walk away.

- **Call the bully out:** If your youngster is confident and secure enough, they can confront the bully by asking why they said what they did. This strategy can be helpful since it puts the bully on the spot and may make them understand that what they're doing is wrong.

Be an Emotionally Available Parent

As a parent, it can be challenging to watch your ADHD child battle with bullying. It is vital to realize, however, that your child is not alone in their experience. Indeed, because of the unique issues they confront in social interactions, many children with ADHD are especially vulnerable to bullying.

To help your child or teen cope with bullying, here are three strategies you can implement.

1. **Validate and support:** To make your child feel validated and supported, remind them that they are not alone and talk to them about their thoughts and experiences. Encourage your youngster to seek help from friends or to participate in activities and projects.

2. **Monitor behavior:** Show your kid how to monitor their own behavior. Help them to see trends in their interactions with others that may lead to bullying and then work with them to develop coping skills.

3. **Connect with peers:** Discuss with teachers how to facilitate connections through school project collaborations or seating near like-minded friends. This can assist your kid in developing strong relationships with their peers, reducing the probability of bullying, and developing a safety plan that includes safe places to go and trustworthy individuals to talk to in the event of bullying.

When you decide to be emotionally available as a parent, this results in parenting that is inclusive and all-encompassing. You must understand that you, as a parent, can only do so much on your own. Keep reading to learn how you can involve others, including other students and teachers, in your child's journey.

Case Study: The Reality of Bullying

Celebrity story: Ryan Gosling

Ryan Gosling, a well-known actor, is a prime example of someone who has overcome bullying and succeeded in his career despite having ADHD. He was diagnosed with ADHD at a young age, faced difficulties in reading and writing, and was often teased by classmates for being different. Despite these challenges, Ryan never gave up on his dreams and worked hard to pursue his passion for acting. With the support of his parents, he was able to channel his energy and creativity into acting and eventually landed a role in the Disney Channel series "The Mickey Mouse Club."

Ryan's success serves as inspiration for children with ADHD who face bullying. He has shown that with hard work, determination, and the right support, anything is possible. By sharing his story, Ryan encourages parents of children with ADHD to provide their children with the support and encouragement they need to pursue their dreams and overcome bullying. Ryan's journey serves as a reminder that children with ADHD can achieve great things with the right support and encouragement.

Esmeralda and Julia

Esmeralda's daughter, Julia, faced challenges as a child with ADHD, including difficulties paying attention in class and being easily distracted. This led to her being bullied by classmates, causing her to come home upset and unwilling to talk about her experiences. But after talking to Julia's teacher, Esmeralda learned that Julia was being bullied by some of her classmates. The girls were teasing her, calling her names, and excluding her from activities.

Esmeralda was determined to help her daughter, and after talking to the school counselor and working with the teacher, they came up with a plan to support Julia. They encouraged her to join clubs and activities, to make new friends and develop her interests, as well as finding ways to improve her focus in class. Over time, Julia became more confident and found a sense of belonging with new friends in the clubs she joined. Esmeralda learned that it takes a community effort to support children with ADHD and was grateful for the help they received from the school and counselor.

Activity

Bullying is a serious issue, and it is important to be aware of the warning signs to ensure that your child is not being affected by it. However, it can be difficult to spot the signs of bullying, especially if your child is not open about their experiences. To help parents better understand what to look for, we've created an easy-to-use checklist of signs that your child might be being bullied. This interactive element will guide you through the warning signs of bullying, making it easier for you to see if your child is being bullied. Remember, your child's well-being is of the utmost importance and you are not alone in your journey to help them.

With this checklist, you can empower yourself with knowledge and take the necessary steps to protect your child. Here is a list of signs that a child is being bullied:

1. unexplainable injuries
2. loss of interest in activities they previously enjoyed
3. changes in eating habits
4. difficulty sleeping
5. decreased self-esteem
6. avoidance of social situations
7. difficulty concentrating in school
8. unexplainable loss or damage of possessions
9. complaints of physical symptoms such as headaches or stomach aches
10. sudden drop in grades
11. self-harm or suicidal thoughts
12. increased fear or anxiety
13. aggressive or disruptive behavior
14. declining relationships with friends and family

It is important to remember that some of these signs may also indicate other issues, so it is always best to have an open and honest conversation with your child about their experiences and feelings. Additionally, if you suspect your child is being bullied, it is important to take their concerns seriously and seek support from school staff, a mental health professional, or law enforcement if necessary.

6

DEALING WITH EMOTIONS

As the parent of a preteen with ADHD, you are aware of the difficulties they encounter in controlling their emotions. You've seen children become angry, stressed, and even upset, but they can learn to manage their emotions with the correct tools. In this chapter, you will discover how to assist your child with ADHD in navigating their emotions and feeling more in control. Practical coping methods, tactics, and mindfulness exercises that have been demonstrated to be useful for children with ADHD will also be presented.

Here are some facts about emotions and ADHD:

- According to research, those with ADHD have more powerful emotions than those who do not have ADHD (Lovering, 2022).
- People with ADHD may struggle to understand and express their emotions, which can cause problems in personal and professional relationships.
- Individuals with ADHD can improve their emotional control skills by practicing mindfulness and other forms of meditation.
- Positive coping methods, such as physical activities and hobbies can also help people with ADHD to regulate their emotions more effectively.

Incorporating these insights into your daily life can help you better understand and control your emotions, resulting in an overall improvement in your well-being and quality of life. Whether your child is feeling overwhelmed, angry, unhappy, or just frustrated, this chapter will provide you with the information you need to support them.

EMOTIONAL HYPERSENSITIVITY AND ADHD

Emotional hypersensitivity is defined as a heightened and powerful emotional reaction to stimuli. People with ADHD frequently suffer from emotional hypersensitivity, which means they are more prone to experience extreme emotions in reaction to various events and situations. ADHD can make emotions stronger and more difficult to manage, causing severe distress and interfering with daily functioning.

Individuals with ADHD feel emotions differently than those who do not have the illness. People with ADHD have been observed to struggle with emotion regulation, frequently experiencing significant mood swings, impulsiveness, and problems handling stress. As a result, they may become impulsive and have difficulty controlling their conduct in response to emotional cues. They may also have a more acute and prolonged emotional reaction to bad situations, resulting in feelings of melancholy and pessimism. People without ADHD, on the other hand, have a more balanced emotional response to stimuli and are better able to regulate their emotions.

Certain situations and lifestyle factors can lead to a less tolerant preteen. Just like when you have a bad day and you feel irritable, for ADHD preteens, these things cause an even higher possibility for outbursts and intolerance.

These are a few things that could worsen your preteen's emotional hypersensitivity.

- **Lack of sleep:** Sleep deprivation has been linked to increased hyperactivity and impulsiveness in ADHD patients. It can also aggravate their emotions, making it even more difficult to regulate and manage them.
- **Stress:** People with ADHD are frequently more susceptible to stress and its effects on their life. Minor stressors can produce considerable emotional upheaval, making it critical to develop appropriate coping skills.
- **Sensory overstimulation:** People with ADHD are frequently hypersensitive to sensory inputs, which can result in extreme emotional reactions. Overstimulation can be caused by a multitude of factors, such as bright lights, loud noises, and strong odors.
- **Hormonal changes:** Adolescents go through a number of hormonal changes, and these changes can have a big impact on their moods. Hormonal fluctuations can be much more pronounced in ADHD patients, leading to increased emotional turbulence.
- **Social pressures:** Bullying and peer pressure are two examples of social pressures that preteens endure. These can result in negative emotions such as despair, rage, and anxiety.

It is necessary for parents to identify these aggravating variables and assist their children in learning how to manage and regulate their emotions. Seeking therapy or counseling, practicing relaxation techniques, and finding strategies to reduce stress are all possible. In those with ADHD, encouraging a healthy sleep schedule, decreasing sensory overstimulation, and addressing social constraints can all help to reduce emotional exacerbation.

IMPORTANCE OF EMOTIONAL REGULATION

The ability to manage and control one's emotions in a healthy and productive manner is referred to as emotional regulation. It is a crucial ability for everyone, but especially for people with ADHD. Emotional management might be difficult for preteens with ADHD. They may, however, learn to better manage their emotions and decrease the influence they have on daily life with the correct tools and tactics in place.

What Is Emotional Regulation?

As the parent of an ADHD preteen, you're probably familiar with the difficulties that come with regulating their emotions. But, exactly what is emotional regulation? It is the process through which we influence the emotions we experience, when we experience them, and how we experience and express them. For instance, when you feel something like frustration, what is your response? Do you cry? Do you lash out? Or do you suppress your frustration and pretend that you are okay? How do you tend to express yourself?

According to Psychology Today (2019), emotional regulation is the ability to exert control over one's own emotional state. This could include evaluating a difficult circumstance in order to minimize anger or anxiety, concealing obvious evidence of sadness or fear, or focusing on reasons to be happy or calm. In the end, you have more power over your own thoughts and feelings with emotional regulation. Since ADHD comes with impulsivity, an ADHD preteen needs the ability to understand and evaluate their emotions in order to react and express themselves appropriately.

Positive psychology believes that we can control and manage our emotions in different ways, whether it's through conscious or unconscious means. It's not about ignoring or hiding our emotions, but instead, it's about having control over them. Emotional regulation skills give us the power to manage our emotions and the ways that we express them. This concept is important for parents to understand as they help their children navigate and validate their emotions.

The ability to manage one's emotions effectively is at the heart of emotional regulation. This involves a number of skills.

- **Awareness:** recognizing and understanding one's emotions, as well as their triggers and effects
- **Control:** managing emotional reactions to prevent them from becoming overwhelming
- **Modulation:** changing the intensity of an emotional response, either by increasing or decreasing it
- **Expression:** expressing emotions in an appropriate and socially acceptable manner
- **Reappraisal:** reframing negative situations or thoughts in a more positive light

- **Coping:** effectively handling and managing stressful emotions, such as anxiety or anger
- **Flexibility:** switching between different emotional states and adjusting emotions to suit different situations

Individuals who have effective emotional regulation skills are better able to manage their emotions and respond to tough situations in a positive and productive manner. As a parent, you should grasp what emotional regulation is and why it is vital for your ADHD adolescent. With this knowledge, you will be more equipped to assist your child in developing emotional regulation abilities and managing their emotions in a healthy manner.

The Benefits of Emotional Regulation

Good emotional regulation abilities can assist children in coping with stress and obstacles, improving their relationships, and improving their general well-being in personal and academic life.

Emotional regulation skills have several beneficial effects on a child's development.

- **Enhancing interpersonal skills:** Children with well-developed emotional regulation are better able to communicate effectively, understand and empathize with others' emotions, and form positive relationships.
- **Developing emotional intelligence:** Good emotional regulation skills contribute to the development of

emotional intelligence, which is the ability to recognize, understand, and manage one's own emotions and the emotions of others. This is a key aspect of success in all areas of life.

- **Taming negative behaviors:** Children with strong emotional regulation are less likely to experience negative behaviors such as outbursts, meltdowns, and other impulsive reactions. They are better equipped to manage their emotions and respond to difficult situations in a calm and composed manner.

- **Improving self-discipline:** Good emotional regulation can help children develop self-discipline skills, including the abilities to control impulses, manage time, and make responsible decisions.

- **Promoting independence:** Children who have mastered emotional regulation become more self-reliant and independent. They are better able to make decisions and handle difficult situations without relying on others.

- **Increasing resilience:** Children who have learned to regulate their emotions are better able to recover from adverse events and have a higher tolerance for frustration. This can help them develop a stronger sense of self and a more positive outlook on life.

By fostering a supportive and understanding environment, parents can help their children develop strong emotional regulation skills that will serve them well throughout their lives.

Helping Your Kid With ADHD Develop or Strengthen Emotional Regulation

Children with ADHD and other associated illnesses frequently struggle with mood management. It is feasible, however, to assist them in developing or strengthening their emotional management skills.

- **Label feelings accurately:** When your child has the vocabulary to express their emotions, they can better process and understand them. This leads to a feeling of being heard and validated, which can decrease their emotional distress.
- **Practice mindfulness meditation:** Mindfulness meditation helps children improve their self-awareness and understanding of the present moment. This can help reduce anxiety and improve their ability to regulate emotions.
- **Provide grounding techniques:** When children feel overwhelmed by their emotions, help them focus on the present moment. This can include deep breathing exercises, progressive muscle relaxation, or sensory grounding activities.
- **Address triggers in advance:** By recognizing triggers that lead to emotional outbursts, children can take steps to prevent or manage them. This can include redirecting their attention, engaging in physical activity, or seeking support from a trusted friend or family member.

- **Encourage self-reflection:** Encouraging children to reflect on their thoughts, feelings, and behaviors can help them understand why they are feeling a certain way and how they can regulate their emotions.
- **Lead by example:** Children learn from examples, so it is crucial to model good self-regulation skills. This can include demonstrating healthy coping mechanisms, managing your own emotions in a constructive way, and seeking help when necessary.
- **Build tolerance for discomfort:** When children can tolerate some level of emotional discomfort, they can learn to regulate their emotions better. You can help by encouraging them to face challenging emotions and experiences and by providing support and encouragement.
- **Create an anger thermometer:** A visual representation of a child's anger intensity can help them understand and regulate it, and see when it is getting too intense.
- **Develop a calm-down plan:** Encouraging children to create a plan for when they become overwhelmed by their emotions can empower them and give them a sense of control.
- **Cultivate anger management skills:** Children with ADHD can benefit from learning anger management skills, such as using deep breathing, progressive muscle relaxation, visualization, or physical activity to defuse anger.
- **Reframe anger:** Encouraging children to see their anger from a different perspective can help reduce its

intensity. For example, they might reframe their anger as frustration, which is less overwhelming.

- **Use deep pressure:** Deep pressure, such as pressure from a weighted blanket or bear hug, can have a calming effect for children with ADHD. This can help regulate emotions and reduce anxiety.

You can assist your child with ADHD to improve or increase their emotional regulation abilities by using some of these tactics. Remember to be patient, consistent, and to offer support and encouragement while they work on managing their emotions. It's vital to remember that development takes time, but your child can learn to regulate their emotions more efficiently with effort and drive.

ANGER MANAGEMENT FOR KIDS WITH ADHD

Children with ADHD frequently struggle with emotion regulation, which can lead to feelings of frustration and rage. These emotions emerge as outbursts, meltdowns, and other undesirable behaviors that can be distressing for both the kid and those around them. Understanding the association between ADHD and rage is critical for establishing effective anger-management strategies for ADHD preteens.

Preteens with ADHD may exhibit rage in a different way than their peers. They may struggle with emotional control and may respond rapidly with extreme anger, which can be overwhelming for them and those around them. As a result, impulsive behavior, acting out, and difficulty sustaining healthy relationships are all possibilities.

Here are a few ways in which anger can manifest in preteens with ADHD.

- **Sudden impulsive outbursts:** Children with ADHD may display intense bursts of anger without considering the consequences.
- **Aggressive behavior:** Physical expressions of anger such as hitting, pushing, or breaking things can occur in kids with ADHD.
- **Self-inflicted harm:** Preteens with ADHD may harm themselves, employing actions such as biting their nails or pulling their hair as a manifestation of their anger.
- **Chronic irritation:** Managing emotions can be challenging for preteens with ADHD and may result in ongoing irritability and anger.
- **Withdrawal:** Children with ADHD may retreat or shut down when overwhelmed by anger and frustration.
- **Defiant attitude:** When struggling with anger, preteens with ADHD may exhibit challenging or defiant behavior.
- **Disruptive conduct:** Acting out anger in a manner that disrupts the class or relationships with others can be seen in kids with ADHD.
- **Anxiety and panic attacks:** Some preteens with ADHD may experience anxiety or panic attacks as a result of their anger.

It's essential to acknowledge that each child with ADHD is unique and may experience rage in a variety of ways. The preceding list is not exhaustive and is simply intended to help parents better understand how rage can appear in their child with ADHD.

It is critical for parents and caregivers to assist preteens with ADHD in developing good anger-management skills. Some strategies that may be beneficial include accurately labeling feelings, mindfulness meditation, grounding exercises, anticipating emotions, increasing self-awareness, modeling self-regulation skills, increasing tolerance for distress, developing a calm-down plan, cultivating anger management skills, reframing anger, and using deep pressure.

Anger is a difficult feeling for anybody to deal with, but it is especially difficult for preteens with ADHD. As a parent, it can be tough to know how to assist your child in managing their anger, but the good news is that there are many successful techniques.

These are a few anger-management strategies that can help preteens with ADHD.

- **Manage anger through exercise**

Engaging in physical activity can be a helpful way to handle anger, as it can serve as a means of improving mood and releasing pent-up energy. Encourage your child, who may struggle with anger due to ADHD, to participate in physical pursuits that they enjoy, such as sports, yoga, or simply going for a walk. The objective is to get them moving and release any negative energy they may be feeling.

- **Reduce screen time**

Preteens with ADHD can often become frustrated with electronics such as television, video games, and smartphones. To help mitigate this, limit your child's screen time and encourage them to participate in alternative activities. You can also establish daily technology-free time for activities like playing board games or reading books.

- **Verbalize feelings**

By teaching your child to express their emotions through words, you can assist them in managing their anger. Encourage them to discuss what they are feeling and why. This can enable them to better understand their emotions and process them in a healthier manner. You can also demonstrate this behavior by talking about your own feelings and how you handle them.

- **Recognize anger as a signal**

It is crucial for your child to comprehend that anger serves as a signal rather than an outcome. Explain to them that anger is a natural response to certain circumstances but it is the way they react to that anger that is important. Teach them healthy coping mechanisms like deep breathing or counting to 10 to help them handle their anger.

- **Avoid physical punishment**

Physical punishment is not a productive way to handle anger in children with ADHD. Instead, concentrate on positive reinforcement and establishing clear boundaries and consequences for negative behavior. Encourage your child to take responsibility for their actions and work with them to find solutions to any problems that may arise.

- **Enhance compromise and negotiation skills**

Developing your child's ability to compromise and negotiate can aid them in managing their anger during challenging situations. Encourage them to listen to the other person's point of view and find a mutually acceptable solution. Engage in role-playing scenarios with your child to help them practice these skills and increase their confidence.

Appropriate Methods of Emotional Expression and Communication

There are three main ways that you can help your preteen express themselves and communicate better.

1. Teaching the Language of Emotions

Parents of ADHD preteens are encouraged to be aware of the significance of teaching their child emotional language. This includes assisting children in identifying and naming various emotions, as well as understanding how each emotion feels in their body. This can be a key step toward assisting youngsters with ADHD in regulating their emotions.

Children with ADHD who understand the language of emotions are better able to explain their feelings to themselves and others. This can be especially beneficial in preventing impulsive or reactive behaviors that are typical in ADHD youngsters. Furthermore, being able to communicate their emotions verbally can assist children with ADHD in understanding their own feelings as well as developing empathy for others.

Start by pointing out different emotions in everyday settings to assist your ADHD adolescent in developing emotional language. For instance, if your child notices someone who appears unhappy, ask them how they believe that person is feeling. Encourage your child to express how they feel as they get more comfortable with identifying emotions. You can also teach kids about emotions and how to express them through books, movies, and other forms of media.

2. Sharing Coping Skills With Your Preteen

Sharing coping strategies with your ADHD adolescent is another technique to help them better regulate their emotions. Teaching them deep breathing exercises, progressive muscle relaxation, and visualization techniques are some examples. These abilities can help children with ADHD calm down when they are agitated or anxious, as well as helping them manage their emotions more efficiently.

In addition to these coping skills, it is necessary to assist your child in developing good behaviors. This can include regular exercise, a balanced diet, and adequate sleep. Children with ADHD can better manage their emotions and be more resilient when faced with stress and obstacles by developing healthy habits.

3. Engaging in Healthy Habits

Another strategy to help teenagers with ADHD regulate their emotions is to engage in good practices. Parents can encourage their child to engage in mindfulness techniques such as meditation and yoga in addition to regular exercise, healthy food, and proper sleep habits. These activities can help children with

ADHD develop greater self-awareness and emotional regulation, and they can be especially beneficial for dealing with anxiety and stress.

Promoting physical activity is another strategy to develop healthy habits. Participating in sports or other physical activities, or simply going on a stroll together might be examples of this. Exercise has been demonstrated to improve mood and well-being in children with ADHD who struggle with impulse control and emotional management.

Finally, by modeling good actions for their children, parents can help them create healthy habits. Eating healthy food, exercising regularly, and making time for self-care are all examples of ways that parents can help their children acquire habits that will benefit their emotional control and well-being.

Case Study: An ADHD Household

Jacob and Elijah are a father-and-son duo who suffer from ADHD and have struggled with anger management. In the past, they felt isolated and helpless due to their explosive tempers and uncontrolled rage, which would often result in outbursts. However, Jacob was determined to help his son overcome this issue and improve their lives. He stumbled upon an article that explained the connection between ADHD and rage, which made him realize the root cause of their problems.

Jacob taught Elijah coping strategies to manage his emotions, such as taking deep breaths and engaging in physical activity. Together, they also joined an ADHD support group, where they received valuable insights and strategies from others facing similar challenges. They sought professional help and received individualized counseling, which helped them better manage their emotions and reactions.

The combination of these strategies and support from their community helped Jacob and Elijah take control of their emotions and anger. They now lead happier, more fulfilling lives and serve as role models for others facing similar challenges. Their story highlights the importance of support and resources for individuals with ADHD to overcome their challenges and lead successful lives.

Activity: Anger Thermometer

One of the most effective methods for teaching children about their feelings is to create an "anger thermometer." This simple tool will help your child understand and recognize when their anger is rising, and it will give them strategies to manage it before it becomes too intense. Here's how to make one.

- **Step 1:** Get materials. You'll need a piece of paper, a pencil, and some crayons or markers.
- **Step 2:** Draw a thermometer. On the left side of the paper, draw a line from the top to the bottom of the page. On the bottom, write "calm." On the top, write "angry."
- **Step 3:** Add color. Use the crayons or markers to color in the thermometer. At the bottom, use a cool color like blue or green. As you go up the thermometer, use a warm color like red or yellow.

- **Step 4:** Explain the thermometer to your child. Explain that the thermometer represents their emotions, with calm at the bottom and anger at the top. The goal is to stay in the blue and green range and use strategies to prevent the anger from getting too high.
- **Step 5:** Identify triggers. Together with your child, write down things that make them angry, such as a sibling taking their toy or a friend not following the rules.
- **Step 6:** Brainstorm strategies. Help your child come up with strategies for managing their anger, such as counting to 10, taking deep breaths, or going for a walk. Write these strategies next to the triggers.
- **Step 7:** Use the thermometer. Encourage your child to use the thermometer when they start to feel angry. Have them rate their anger on a scale of 1–10, and then use the strategies they wrote down to help manage their emotions.

By using the anger thermometer regularly, your child will learn to recognize their triggers and develop coping skills to manage their anger. This is a great tool for parents to help their preteens better understand and manage their emotions.

7

CALMING THE CHAOS THROUGH STRUCTURE

B y now, you've learned about different ways to help your child manage their emotions and understand their ADHD better. It's not uncommon for children with ADHD to feel overwhelmed and disorganized, but structure can provide a sense of stability and routine that can make all the difference. Take Lily's story for instance. Lily was a high school student with ADHD. Despite her struggles with focus and attention, she refused to let her diagnosis define her. Instead, she used her ADHD to her advantage and found creative ways to manage her schoolwork.

Lily discovered that she was able to multitask effectively, and she learned how to balance multiple projects at once. She found that she was able to complete her schoolwork quickly and efficiently, often finishing assignments before her classmates. Lily's classmates marveled at her ability to handle such a heavy workload, and her teachers took notice of her dedication and hard work. Lily proved that with a positive attitude and a willingness to work hard, anyone with ADHD can succeed.

BUILDING A ROUTINE

Developing a routine might be challenging for a parent of an ADHD child, but it is essential for managing symptoms and assisting your child in being productive and high-functioning. A consistent routine can enhance organizational abilities, increase focus, and reduce impulsiveness.

A routine can provide structure that an ADHD child may find difficult to develop on their own. An ADHD youngster can feel more secure and in control by following a structured routine for meals, activities, and bedtime. This framework can also aid in reducing distractions and increasing focus. For example, if your child knows that homework is due right after supper, they will be less distracted and will be able to complete their schoolwork more quickly.

Developing a routine should be a joint effort between parent and child. Encourage your child to contribute ideas and suggestions for their daily routine. This way, your child will experience a feeling of ownership and accountability over their schedule. Also, be adaptable and open to making modifications if the routine isn't working.

Why Is it Important?

As a parent of a preteen with ADHD, you are well aware that managing their disease can be a constant battle. However, one of the most effective methods to help your child thrive is to establish a schedule for them. An organized daily schedule provides a sense of stability and predictability, which can be incredibly beneficial for children with ADHD.

Research has shown that kids with ADHD respond well to routines because they provide clear expectations and boundaries, making it easier for them to focus and complete tasks (Low, 2022). Routines also help children with ADHD manage their time and prioritize responsibilities, reducing feelings of stress and anxiety. Additionally, routines help to regulate sleep patterns and improve overall physical and emotional health.

Having a routine in place can also promote better communication and cooperation between you and your child. By establishing a set schedule, you can work together to make sure that your child is able to attend to their responsibilities, prioritize their time, and get the support they need to succeed.

TIPS TO HELP YOUR CHILD DEVELOP A ROUTINE OR SCHEDULE

A routine can provide structure and stability for children with ADHD, helping them to manage their symptoms and succeed in their daily lives. As a parent, there are several tips you can follow to help your child establish a routine that works for them.

1. Let your child help make the routine

Involve them in the process of creating a routine so they feel ownership and responsibility for following it. This can be especially helpful if they have input on what activities they'd like to include. By allowing them to take part in the creation of their routine, they can feel more invested in following through with it.

2. Be realistic about time and priorities

Consider your child's schedule, including school, after-school activities, and responsibilities, and make sure to allocate enough time for everything. Prioritize the most important activities and make adjustments if necessary. It's important to be mindful of the amount of time each task or activity requires and to allocate sufficient time to allow for smooth transitions.

3. Provide limited choices

It can be overwhelming for children with ADHD to have too many choices, so provide a few options for them to choose from. This way, they still feel like they have some control, but they are not completely overwhelmed. Limiting choices can reduce anxiety and stress, which can have a positive impact on behavior and attention.

4. Be specific

Be clear and specific about what your child needs to do and when. Use language that is easy for them to understand so you can avoid ambiguity. Clear instructions can increase the likelihood that tasks are completed correctly and efficiently.

5. Make time for movement

Children with ADHD always benefit from physical activity, so try to include some form of movement in their routine, such as a quick walk or stretch. Movement can help improve focus, attention, and reduce symptoms of ADHD.

6. Be flexible

It's important to be open to change and flexible with your child's routine. Don't be afraid to make adjustments if something isn't working or if your child's needs change. Being adaptable can help you maintain an effective and relevant routine over time.

7. Include visual cues

Using visual cues such as pictures or illustrations can help children with ADHD to better understand their routine and follow it more effectively. Visual aids can also make the routine more appealing and engaging for children.

8. Set a timer and alarms

Set alarms or timers to help your child transition from one activity to the next and stay on track with their routine. Timers can provide a visual and auditory prompt that helps children understand when it's time to switch activities.

9. Suggested routines

Consider starting with a routine for morning, after school, dinner, and bedtime. This will provide structure and predictability for your child throughout the day. Having established routines can provide a sense of security and reduce feelings of uncertainty and stress.

With these tips in mind, you can work together with your child to develop a routine that works for them and helps them succeed in their daily life.

School Strategies

As a parent of an ADHD preteen, you are no doubt aware of the importance of building a routine for your child. But what about at school? School can be a chaotic and stressful environment for children with ADHD, making it even more important to develop strategies that can help them succeed. By implementing a few simple, effective strategies in the classroom, you can help your child become a more organized and confident learner.

In this section, we will delve into the specific school strategies that can help your child achieve success. These strategies have been proven to work in classrooms around the world and can be customized to fit your child's individual needs and strengths. By using these strategies, you can help your child build a routine that will not only calm the chaos in the classroom, but will also help them reach their full potential. So, whether your child is just starting school or well into their academic career, don't hesitate to explore the strategies that can help them succeed.

These are a few strategies that you can implement right now.

- **Create a homework-only space at home**

Having a place to do homework set out for your child might help them focus and avoid distractions. Make sure the space is peaceful, well-lit, and equipped with everything they'll need to study, such as a desk, chair, and materials. Encourage your child to do their homework in the same spot every day, since consistency can help them build a pattern.

- **Create a consistent schedule**

Developing a routine and sticking to a schedule can be quite beneficial for children with ADHD. Establish a homework and studying plan, include specific times for breaks, and stick to it every day. A regular routine gives children with ADHD greater control, decreases stress, and increases focus.

- **Get the teacher involved**

Teachers can play an important role in assisting your child with ADHD to succeed in school. Communicate with the teacher on a frequent basis to discuss your child's progress and any difficulties they may be experiencing. Teachers can also give practical advice and make concessions to help your child succeed in school.

- **Get organized**

Organization is essential for children with ADHD because it allows them to stay focused and avoid distractions. Encourage your child to organize their supplies, homework, and books in a style that makes sense to them. Providing your child with a planner or calendar can also be very beneficial, as it can help them keep track of assignments and due dates.

- **Equip them with tools**

Giving your child the correct tools can help them focus and complete their jobs more efficiently. Consider purchasing a planner or calendar, additional pens and paper, concentration aids such as noise-canceling headphones, and recording applications to assist them in taking notes and staying organized.

- **Keep expectations consistent**

When it comes to setting expectations for your child, consistency is essential. Make clear what you expect from them in terms of grades, behavior, and effort, and convey it to the teacher. Keeping expectations consistent will prevent confusion and help your youngster focus.

- **Limit distractions**

Distractions should be kept to a minimum for children with ADHD. Encourage your youngster to switch off their phone and restrict their screen use during homework and study time. Providing a distraction-free study place can help your youngster stay focused long enough to complete their work.

- **Provide frequent feedback**

Giving your child regular feedback might help them stay on course and feel more in charge. When they're doing well, give them praise, and when they need to improve, give them constructive criticism. This can help them gain confidence and feel more motivated to succeed.

- **Reward good behavior**

Children with ADHD can benefit greatly from rewards. Small rewards should be given for good behavior, such as increased screen time, a special food, or a fun activity. This can help to reinforce great conduct and inspire your youngster to work hard in the future.

- **Give them a break**

It's essential that you give your child a break, especially if they're feeling overwhelmed. Encourage them to take small pauses from their homework and studies to indulge in physical activities such as stretching or going for a stroll. Regular breaks can help reduce stress and enhance focus, allowing your child to be more productive when they return to work.

Time Management

Time management is an important skill that can assist an ADHD adolescent in developing a schedule and establishing structure in their daily life. ADHD can make it difficult to concentrate, stay organized, and finish assignments on time. You may help your child prioritize their tasks, set objectives, and learn to manage their time more efficiently by teaching them time management skills. This, in turn, will assist them in developing a routine and improving their behavior.

There are various advantages to time management for ADHD preteens. It can help them reduce stress and worry, enhance their grades, boost their self-esteem, and even develop a more positive attitude. They can prioritize their duties, accomplish them on time, and avoid feeling overwhelmed if they use good time management. Additionally, learning to manage their time well can help them establish routines and habits that will serve them into adulthood.

Begin by teaching your child the fundamentals of planning, prioritizing, and scheduling to help them develop strong time management skills. Encourage them to set goals and devise a plan for achieving those goals. Give them tools, like a calendar or a to-do list, as well as coaching and assistance as they learn to manage their time properly. Your child may acquire habits and build a routine that will help them achieve success in school and in life with a little patience and assistance.

As a parent of an ADHD preteen, you understand the importance of time management in helping your child develop a routine. These strategies are designed to help your child stay organized and on track throughout the day:

- **Setting routines is a key aspect of time management for ADHD preteens.** This can include having a set time for waking up, eating breakfast, doing homework, and going to bed. This structure provides a sense of predictability that can help your child feel more in control and less overwhelmed.
- **Eliminating dawdling is also important in time management.** Encourage your child to start and finish tasks in a timely manner, taking breaks only as needed. This can help your child avoid procrastination and stay focused on what needs to be done.

- **Organizing work spaces can also help your child manage their time more effectively.** Encourage your child to keep their workspace tidy and free of distractions, such as clutter and unnecessary items.
- **It's also helpful to encourage your child to make a list of everything they do during the week.** Create a schedule and make a to-do list. Having a written plan can help your child prioritize their tasks and stay on track throughout the day.
- **Try to make boring activities fun:** You can turn repetitive and structured activities into a game or find ways to make them more interesting for your preteen, to encourage them to stay on task and on time.

By following these tips and strategies, you can help your ADHD preteen develop effective time management skills and build a routine that will serve them well in their daily life.

Concentration, Completing Tasks, and Avoiding Procrastination

Children with ADHD often struggle with staying focused, retaining information, and managing their time effectively. This can lead to procrastination and the feeling of being overwhelmed by tasks. However, there are steps you can take to help your child build these essential skills.

Encourage good sleeping habits:

- Set a consistent bedtime and wake-up time.
- Avoid screens and bright lights before bed.
- Create a relaxing bedtime routine.

Make dietary changes:

- Incorporate more nutrient-dense foods like fruit, vegetables, and whole grains.
- Limit sugar and processed foods.
- Encourage regular and consistent meal times.

Practice mindfulness with them:

- Engage in deep breathing exercises.
- Practice positive self-talk.
- Encourage regular meditation or yoga.

Introduce them to music:

- Encourage listening to music in the background while working.
- Encourage playing an instrument to improve focus and concentration.

Engage them in more outdoor activities:

- Encourage regular physical activity.
- Spend time in nature, doing things like hiking or gardening.

Concentration Exercises

1. **The coin game:** Have your child place a coin in their non-dominant hand, then try to transfer it to the other hand without dropping it.
2. **Relaxation and positive imagery:** Have your child close their eyes and imagine a relaxing scene or positive scenario.
3. **Mind-body integration:** Encourage activities that improve coordination and balance like dancing or tai chi.
4. **Crossword puzzles:** Encourage your child to complete crossword puzzles regularly to improve their focus and concentration.
5. **Memory games:** Encourage your child to play memory games to improve their memory and focus.
6. **Dancing sequence games:** Encourage your child to follow dance sequences to improve recall and coordination.
7. **Mazes:** Encourage your child to complete mazes to improve their focus and problem-solving skills.
8. **Puzzle games:** Encourage your child to play puzzle games to improve concentration and problem-solving.

9. **Paddleball:** Encourage your child to play paddleball to improve hand-eye coordination and focus.

Here are some additional things you can do to keep your ADHD child on track.

- **Jump right into projects:** Encourage your child to start their work immediately, rather than procrastinating.
- **Limit directions to one or two at a time:** Give clear and simple directions to your child, rather than overwhelming them with too many tasks.
- **Set a timer:** Encourage your child to set a timer for a specific period of time, then take a short break before continuing.
- **Be open to what works:** Encourage your child to try different methods of improving focus and concentration, and see what works best for them.
- **Direct focus back to the task:** When your child becomes distracted, encourage them to refocus on the task at hand.

Other ways to help your child focus:

- Discover different types of fidgets, including ones you can make.
- Try free graphic organizers to help your child get through reading, writing, and math assignments.
- Learn ways to break down writing assignments so they're easier to focus on.

Case Study: Mandy and Katie

Meet Mandy and her daughter, Katie. Mandy was searching for ways to help her daughter, who had been diagnosed with ADHD, to concentrate better. One day, she read an article about the benefits of using fidgets in the classroom for children with ADHD. Mandy decided to give it a try and bought a set of classroom-friendly fidgets for Katie to use during her classes. To her delight, the fidgets were very effective, and Katie was able to focus and pay attention better in class, leading to improvement in her grades.

Additionally, Mandy wanted to keep Katie physically active, so she enrolled her in gymnastics classes. This physical activity also helped Katie concentrate and focus better, and she was able to complete her tasks more efficiently. Mandy was grateful to have found these simple but effective strategies to help her daughter. She shared her success with other parents who were facing similar challenges with their children. With determination and the right strategies, Mandy and Katie were able to overcome their struggles and improve Katie's focus and concentration, leading to better academic and personal outcomes.

Activity: Create a Schedule

Creating a schedule for a child with ADHD can be a daunting task, but it's essential for their overall success in managing their symptoms and staying focused. By having a routine in place, children with ADHD can feel more organized and in control, reducing stress and improving their ability to concentrate.

Here's a step-by-step guide to help you and your preteen create a schedule that works best for them.

1. **Identify the most critical tasks:** Write down the must-do tasks such as school work, meals, and bedtime. These are the non-negotiable items that should be part of your child's daily schedule.

2. **Get your child involved:** Encourage your child to take an active role in creating their schedule. Ask them what activities they enjoy doing, and let them pick the times they'd like to do them. This way, they'll feel more invested in the schedule and be more likely to stick to it.

3. **Make time for physical activity:** Including physical activity in the schedule is essential for children with ADHD. It helps release excess energy and improves concentration. Consider scheduling time for outdoor activities, sports, or even just a short walk around the block.

4. **Be flexible:** A rigid schedule may not work for every child with ADHD. Be open to adjusting the schedule as needed and be willing to make changes if something isn't working.

5. **Use visual aids:** Using a visual schedule, such as a whiteboard or a planner, can be helpful for children with ADHD. It helps them see their day at a glance and provides a visual reminder of what needs to be done.

6. **Reward good behavior:** Positive reinforcement is an excellent way to encourage your child to stick to the schedule. Consider offering rewards for following the schedule or for completing tasks on time.

7. **Establish a routine:** Stick to the schedule as much as possible. A consistent routine can help reduce anxiety and increase focus.

Creating a schedule with your child is a collaborative process that requires patience and understanding. By working together, you can create a routine that helps your child manage their ADHD and improve their ability to focus. Don't be afraid to make changes or try new things—what works for one child might not work for another. The most important thing is to find what works best for your child and stick with it.

8

SETTING THEM UP FOR SUCCESS WITH LIFE SKILLS

As your child grows and moves closer toward adulthood, it's crucial that they develop the skills needed to live independently and confidently. This chapter is designed to help you understand the importance of these life skills and how you can support your child in acquiring them.

For children with ADHD, mastering these life skills can be a challenge, so it is all the more important that they learn them as early as possible. Having a strong foundation in these essential skills can help them navigate the challenges of everyday life, and give them the confidence they need to succeed.

WHAT ARE LIFE SKILLS?

Life skills are an important aspect of growing up and becoming an independent and productive member of society. The World Health Organization defines life skills as abilities for adaptive and positive behavior that allow individuals to effectively handle the demands and challenges of everyday life (2020). Essentially, life skills are the building blocks that prepare young individuals to live on their own and succeed in the world.

While some individuals may naturally develop life skills as they grow and mature, it is crucial for parents to actively support their child's growth in this area. This can include helping them develop essential skills such as problem solving, communication, time management, and more.

Whether it's navigating daily tasks or handling conflicts and obstacles that arise, life skills play a significant role in a child's ability to thrive in the world. By understanding what life skills are and how they can support their child's development, parents can help set them up for a successful and fulfilling future.

THE IMPORTANCE OF LIFE SKILLS

Life skills are crucial for preteens with ADHD, as they help them become independent, self-sufficient, and confident individuals. The development of life skills enables young people to handle the demands and challenges of everyday life effectively, preparing them for adulthood. Here are some of the reasons why life skills are so important for preteens with ADHD.

- **Promotes independence and self-sufficiency:** By learning life skills, preteens with ADHD are equipped with the necessary abilities to take care of themselves, solve problems, and make decisions. They learn how to manage their time, finances, and household chores, which helps to reduce their dependence on others.

- **Builds confidence:** When preteens with ADHD develop life skills, they become more confident in their abilities. This boost in confidence allows them to feel more in control of their lives and to face new challenges more easily.
- **Encourages personal responsibility:** By developing life skills, preteens with ADHD learn to take responsibility for their own lives. They understand that their actions have consequences and that they must take responsibility for their mistakes. This helps them to learn a sense of accountability and to make better decisions in the future.
- **Improves decision-making skills:** Preteens with ADHD who develop life skills are better equipped to make informed decisions. They learn to weigh options and consider the consequences of their actions. This helps them to make better choices, which can lead to a more fulfilling life.
- **Prepares for adulthood:** Life skills are essential for young people as they transition into adulthood. By learning life skills, preteens with ADHD are better equipped to navigate the challenges of adulthood, such as managing finances, finding employment, and maintaining relationships.

Life skills are an essential part of a preteen's development, especially for those with ADHD. They help to promote independence, build confidence, encourage personal responsibility, improve decision-making skills, and prepare young people for adulthood. By helping preteens with ADHD to develop life skills, parents are setting them up for success in the future.

Decision Making

One of the core challenges for individuals with ADHD is making good decisions, especially when it comes to complex and time-sensitive situations. ADHD can affect a person's ability to weigh options, follow through on tasks, and make choices that align with their long-term goals. However, with the right guidance and support, it is possible to help preteens with ADHD develop strong decision-making skills.

How to Help Your Child Master Decision Making

- **Thinking of possible solutions:** Encourage your child to generate a list of potential solutions to any problem they are facing.
- **Brainstorming:** You can help your child by conducting a brainstorming session where you both come up with as many ideas as possible.
- **Using games:** Using games that require quick thinking and problem-solving can be a fun way to help your child develop their decision-making skills.
- **Using the problem-solving wheel:** The problem-solving wheel is a tool that helps individuals break a problem down into smaller parts, making it easier to find a solution.

- **Letting them resolve conflicts:** Instead of taking over, act as a mediator. Help your child to understand both sides of a situation and let them come to a decision on their own.
- **Push them to make choices:** Give your child opportunities to make their own choices, even if they are small ones. This will help them build confidence in their ability to make decisions.
- **Let them experience the natural consequences:** Allowing your child to experience the consequences of their choices, whether good or bad, will help them learn from their experiences and make better decisions in the future.

Step-by-Step Guide You Can Teach Your Kids

1. **Define the problem:** Teach your child to identify the problem they are facing and to define it as clearly as possible.
2. **Write down their thoughts:** Encourage your child to write down their thoughts and ideas, this will help them to organize and clarify their thoughts.
3. **Make a list:** Encourage your child to create a list of potential solutions, this will help them to weigh their options and decide on the best course of action.
4. **Find a quiet space:** Encourage your child to find a quiet space where they can focus on making a decision.
5. **Create a deadline:** Teach your child to create a deadline for making a decision, this will help them to prioritize and decide in a timely manner.

6. **Limit their choices:** Teach your child to limit the number of choices they have to make, this will help them focus on the most important options and make a decision more quickly.

7. **Ask for help:** Encourage your child to ask for help when they need it, this could be from friends, family, or a teacher.

8. **Celebrate good decisions:** Finally, encourage your child to celebrate their good decisions, this will reinforce the positive behavior and make it more likely to continue.

Creative Thinking

There is a growing body of research that suggests a strong link between creativity and ADHD. Many people with ADHD have an innate ability to think outside the box and come up with unique and innovative ideas. ADHD can bring with it a heightened level of impulsiveness and hyperactivity that can drive individuals to think creatively. However, it's important to note that creativity is not a direct symptom of ADHD, and not everyone with ADHD will necessarily be creative.

As a parent, you can help your child with ADHD tap into their creative potential by engaging them in activities that encourage imaginative thinking.

- **Ask interesting questions:** Encourage your child to think critically and ask questions about the world around them.
- **Use project-based learning:** Encourage your child to participate in hands-on projects that allow them to think creatively and use their imagination.
- **Do something new and unexpected:** Encourage your child to try new things and engage in activities that challenge their creativity.
- **Bring in artifacts:** Use objects, images, and other artifacts to stimulate your child's imagination and encourage them to think creatively.

- **Put on role plays:** Encourage your child to act out scenarios and play different roles to engage their imagination and encourage more creative thinking.
- **Activate the imagination:** Encourage your child to use their imagination to engage in activities that allow them to explore their creative potential.

Other Tips to Consider

To foster creative thinking in your child with ADHD, consider these additional tips.

- **Encourage group activities:** Joining creative group activities can provide a supportive environment for your child to express their imagination and collaborate with others.
- **Identify strengths:** Helping your child recognize their own strengths can increase their confidence and enhance their creative abilities.
- **Use real-life examples:** Showing your child examples of people with ADHD who have successful careers in creative fields can serve as inspiration and motivation.
- **Don't correct every error:** Avoid being too quick to correct your child's mistakes. Instead, encourage them to take risks and view mistakes as opportunities for learning and growth.
- **Dedicate space and resources:** Providing your child with a dedicated space and the necessary resources for creative activities will allow them to fully express their imagination and continue to grow their skills.

CHORES

It can be challenging for children with ADHD to complete chores, but with the right strategies in place, it can be done. Chores can help teach children with ADHD valuable life skills, like organization and responsibility. They also give kids structure and accountability in their lives. Since it is hard for ADHD preteens to focus and stay on task, completing a chore can be a little bit of a victory for them.

Getting Them to Do Chores

Here are some tips to help your child with ADHD get started with chores.

- **Use visual aids:** Provide a visual way to keep track of chores and progress.
- **Separate tasks:** Break down tasks into smaller, more manageable parts.
- **Keep a neat home:** Organize your home to make it easier for your child to learn and complete chores.
- **Create incentives:** Offer incentives for completing tasks to encourage your child.
- **Make deadlines:** Set deadlines for completing tasks to break them up and make them more manageable.
- **Allow for flexibility:** Give your child some choice by allowing a little flexibility in their chores.
- **Provide assistance:** Be ready to assist your child when they need it.

- **Show encouragement:** Encourage and reward your child for a job well done.
- **Verbalize consequences:** Explain the consequences of not completing chores to help your child understand their responsibility.
- **Change rewards:** Switch up the rewards to keep your child motivated.
- **Keep watch:** Observe your child to get to know their strengths and challenges when it comes to chores.
- **Manage expectations:** Manage your expectations and be realistic about what your child can do.
- **Engage in positive talk:** Avoid using negative words like "chores," "jobs," "responsibility," or "work." Instead, ask for their help.
- **Start small:** Start with small, manageable chores and gradually increase the difficulty.
- **Avoid getting angry:** Don't get angry or frustrated with your child if they struggle with chores.
- **Make it urgent yet fun:** Make chores feel urgent and enjoyable to encourage your child to participate.

Age-Appropriate Chores

The age at which children can start doing chores will vary, but typically, executive function skills start to develop around the age of four or five. Here is a list of age-appropriate chores based on the child's executive function, not their chronological age.

- **Ages 4–5:** simple tasks such as putting away toys and making their bed
- **Ages 6–7:** more involved tasks such as setting the table, clearing the dishes, and folding laundry
- **Ages 8–9:** tasks such as sweeping, vacuuming, and helping with grocery shopping
- **Ages 10–12:** more complex tasks like doing laundry, taking out the trash, and cleaning bathrooms

- **Ages 13 and up:** advanced tasks such as cooking, yard work, and household budgeting

Case Study: The Tale of Two Families

This is about two families who have children with ADHD and the challenges they face in getting them to help with household chores. The first family has a son named Max and the second family has a daughter named Elizabeth. Both families were determined to find ways to make chores easier and more manageable for their children.

Max's parents adopted a structured approach by breaking down tasks into smaller pieces, providing him with a visual chart, organizing their home to be more conducive to learning, and setting deadlines to help him stay focused. They also offered incentives and encouragement, explained the consequences of not completing chores, and changed up the rewards to keep Max engaged.

Elizabeth's parents took a more relaxed approach by avoiding negative language and making chores fun. They started small and adapted their approach to Elizabeth's age and abilities, observing her and getting to know her to find out what worked best. As Elizabeth grew up, her parents gradually increased the difficulty and variety of tasks, making sure they were age-appropriate. By creating a fun and positive environment, they were able to teach Elizabeth about responsibility and independence, and she eventually started to enjoy helping out around the house.

Both Max and Elizabeth's families found success in helping their children with ADHD manage their household chores, and they adapted their approach over time to match the children's changing abilities and needs. They showed that with a little patience, creativity, and understanding, children with ADHD can learn to become responsible and independent.

Activity: Creating a Chore Chart

Creating a chore chart for your ADHD preteen can be a fun and interactive process that helps to establish routines and promote responsibility. Here's a simple guide to get started.

1. **Get your child involved:** Involve your child in the creation of the chore chart by asking them to help identify tasks they can do around the house. This will make them feel a sense of ownership and responsibility.
2. **Make a list of tasks:** Together, make a list of age-appropriate tasks your child can complete. Be sure to break down complex tasks into smaller, more manageable components.
3. **Choose a visual format:** Decide on a visual format such as a whiteboard or a paper sheet for the chore chart. You can use online tools like Goally to create a digital chart that your child can access on a tablet or smartphone.
4. **Assign tasks:** Assign each task to a specific day of the week or specific time of day. Make sure the chart is easy to read and understand.

5. **Offer incentives:** Offer incentives such as screen time or allowance for completed tasks. Change up the rewards to keep things fresh and exciting.

6. **Set deadlines:** Set deadlines for each task to keep your child on track. Allow a little flexibility, but be firm on the deadlines so that your child learns the importance of completing tasks on time.

7. **Review and adjust:** Regularly review and adjust the chart with your child. Be open to feedback and make changes as needed to ensure the chart is working for your child.

8. **Celebrate successes:** Celebrate your child's successes and encourage them for a job well done. This will help build confidence and motivate them to continue doing their best.

By following these steps, you can create a chore chart that works for your ADHD preteen and helps them develop responsibility and a sense of accomplishment.

9

DON'T FORGET—YOU MATTER, TOO

As a parent of a child with ADHD, you are no stranger to the demands of caregiving. You pour your heart and soul into your child's well-being, but it's important to remember that you can't pour from an empty cup. Just like the instructions given on airplanes, you need to put the oxygen mask on yourself first before helping your child.

This chapter is dedicated to reminding you that you matter too. It's time to prioritize your own happiness and health so that you can be the best parent possible. Taking care of yourself doesn't have to be complicated or time-consuming. Simple steps can make a big difference in your well-being. So, take a deep breath, relax, and let's dive into the world of self-care.

WHAT IS SELF-CARE?

Self-care is a vital aspect of a healthy lifestyle, especially for parents of children with ADHD. It encompasses all the actions you take to improve your overall health and well-being. It is critical to understand that self-care doesn't mean indulging in selfish behavior. Instead, it is a deliberate effort to prioritize your own needs and make sure you have the necessary resources to provide the best possible care for your child.

Self-care encompasses six umbrella categories, including physical, psychological, emotional, spiritual, social, and professional. By prioritizing these areas, you can ensure that you are healthy, happy, and able to provide the support and care that your child needs.

1. Physical self-care

This entails taking care of your body. It includes eating a balanced diet, getting regular exercise, and getting enough sleep. Exercise can help reduce stress, increase energy levels, and improve your mood, which is essential for parents of children with ADHD. Making sure that you get enough sleep is also crucial, as it helps to improve your focus, concentration, and memory.

2. Psychological self-care

This is about taking care of your mental health. It includes activities like mindfulness, meditation, therapy, and journaling.

Psychologists have shown that therapy can help reduce stress and improve mood, which is particularly important for parents who are dealing with the added stress of caring for a child with ADHD.

3. Emotional self-care

This is about taking care of your emotional well-being. It can include anything from spending time with friends and family to engaging in activities that bring you joy (like painting or reading). When you prioritize your emotional well-being, you'll feel more balanced and centered, which will help you better manage the stress and demands of caring for your child.

4. Spiritual self-care

Employ practices that help you connect with your inner self, such as yoga or meditation. This type of self-care can bring a sense of peace and clarity, which is crucial for parents who are feeling overwhelmed and stressed.

5. Social self-care

Maintain healthy relationships with friends and family. It is important to prioritize these relationships, as they provide an essential support system for parents of children with ADHD. This type of self-care can include things like regular phone calls with friends, spending time with family, or participating in a support group for parents of children with ADHD.

6. Professional self-care

This is about ensuring a healthy work-life balance. For many parents, work can be a source of stress and anxiety or an escape from that at home, but it is important to find ways to balance your work and personal life. This type of self-care can include things like delegating tasks, setting boundaries, and taking breaks.

Why Is Self-Care Important for Parents?

Self-care is a vital aspect of parenting, and it is crucial for parents of ADHD preteens to prioritize their own well-being. Regular self-care activities allow you to recharge and rejuvenate, making it easier for you to tackle the daily challenges that come with raising a child. By focusing on your own needs, you'll be better equipped to provide the best possible care for your child.

Studies have shown that parents who engage in self-care are better equipped to manage their child's challenging behavior (Pfiffner & Haack, 2014). They are calmer and more patient in stressful situations, which allows them to be present and attentive with their children. Additionally, parents who prioritize self-care find it easier to find joy and strength in the good times, and they are better equipped to handle difficult times.

Taking care of yourself as a parent of an ADHD preteen is essential to ensuring that your family is healthy and happy. Here are four specific benefits that can result from prioritizing self-care.

1. Managing challenging behavior

Parents who engage in regular self-care activities are better equipped to handle their child's challenging behavior. This might involve taking a few deep breaths or going for a quick walk to clear their mind when their child is acting out. By taking care of their own needs, parents can remain calm and level-headed, allowing them to respond to their child's behavior in a more effective manner.

2. Staying calm in stressful moments

Life as a parent of an ADHD child can be stressful, and it's important to have ways to cope with this stress. This might involve practicing mindfulness or meditation, seeking support from a trusted friend or family member, or simply taking a few moments each day to focus on one's breathing. By engaging in activities that help them feel calm and relaxed, parents can stay centered even when their child's behavior is causing stress.

3. Being present with their children

When parents are caught up in their own stress and worries, it can be difficult for them to be fully present with their children. Engaging in self-care activities such as taking yoga classes or going for walks can help parents feel more centered and grounded, allowing them to be more present with their children.

4. Being patient

Parenting can be a challenging and demanding task, and it's important to have the patience and resilience to handle difficult situations. Engaging in self-care activities, such as reading a book, taking a bath, or simply taking a moment to relax, can help parents recharge their batteries and find the patience they need to handle their child's behavior.

PRACTICING SELF-CARE

Self-care is an essential aspect of a healthy lifestyle. As a parent of an ADHD preteen, it's essential to take care of yourself so that you can give your best to your child. This section will provide you with a list of tips for actions that you can take to practice self-care and be the best version of yourself. From carving out time for yourself to planning for your future, each tip is meant to help you prioritize yourself and your health.

So, take a moment to read and implement the suggestions that resonate with you.

- **Carve out your time:** This means setting aside some time for yourself, just like you would for your child or other responsibilities. You can make time for yourself by waking up earlier, staying up later, or even taking a few moments throughout the day to do something that you enjoy.
- **Set priorities:** Make sure you prioritize your needs and make time for self-care activities. Write down a list of things you want to achieve and work on them.
- **Choose fun things to do in advance:** Having something fun to look forward to can help break up the monotony of daily life. Plan activities that bring you joy and happiness.
- **Spend time with family and friends:** Surround yourself with people who care about you and make you feel good. Having a support system is crucial to your well-being.

- **Find folks to take care of you:** Ask for help when you need it. You don't have to do everything on your own.
- **Get out of the house:** Take a walk, go to a museum or spend time in nature. Spending time outside can help clear your mind and reduce stress.
- **Pamper yourself:** Treat yourself to a spa day, get a massage, or even just take a relaxing bath. Do something special for yourself.
- **See your doctor regularly:** Regular check-ups with your doctor can help catch any potential health issues before they become serious.
- **Stay organized:** A cluttered and disorganized space can lead to stress. Make sure your environment is organized and tidy.
- **Plan for your future:** Make sure you have a plan for your future and take the necessary steps to reach your goals. This can bring peace of mind and a sense of purpose to your life.

Self-Care Activities for Parents

Self-care is an important aspect of a parent's life, yet it is often neglected due to the demands of everyday existence. However, taking care of yourself is not a selfish act, but a necessary one that can help you feel refreshed and rejuvenated.

Here are some self-care activities that you can try right now to give yourself some much-needed time and attention.

- **Meditate:** Taking slow, deep breaths can help you calm your mind and reduce stress. Try starting your day with a few minutes of meditation or taking a break for meditation during the day when you need it.
- **Spend time in nature:** Spending time in nature, whether it's going for a walk in the park, or simply sitting and taking in the sights and sounds of the great outdoors, can be very rejuvenating for the mind and soul.
- **Call a friend who will listen:** Sometimes it can be cathartic to simply chat with a friend who will listen and let you debrief your day. Having someone to talk to can help you feel less isolated and more secure.
- **Spend quality time with your partner or friend:** Spending time with those close to you can be a great way to recharge and strengthen your relationships.
- **Listen to music:** Listening to music that you enjoy can be a simple way to uplift your mood and provide a moment of peace and tranquility.
- **Join a book club:** Reading and discussing books with others can be a great way to learn and connect with those who have similar interests.
- **Go for a walk:** Going for a walk can be a great way to get some exercise, enjoy nature, and get some fresh air.
- **Write in a gratitude journal:** Writing down what you're grateful for can help you reduce stress and focus on the positives in your life.
- **Take a break from gadgets:** Taking a break from technology can help you reduce tension and be more present in the moment.

- **Practice mindfulness:** Mindfulness can help you reduce stress, increase focus, and improve overall well-being.
- **Get some physical exercise:** Regular exercise can help you reduce stress, increase energy levels, and improve your overall physical and mental health.
- **Eat well:** Eating a healthy and balanced diet can provide you with the energy and nutrients you need to feel your best.
- **Shop local:** Supporting local businesses can be a great way to help your community and reduce stress by reducing the amount of time you spend shopping.
- **Practice meditation:** Meditation can help you reduce tension, increase focus, and improve overall well-being.
- **Find your tribe:** Connecting with others who are facing similar challenges can be a great way to find support, understanding, and a sense of community.
- **Learn acceptance:** Learning to accept yourself and your situation can help you reduce stress and find peace in the moment.
- **Keep the lines of communication open between your spouse:** Good communication with your spouse can help you feel more connected and reduce stress in your relationship.
- **Compliment yourself:** Taking time to acknowledge and appreciate your own strengths and achievements can help you build confidence and reduce stress.
- **Do something nice for yourself every day:** Taking care of yourself can help you feel better and reduce stress. Doing something small for yourself every day,

like taking a bath or buying yourself a treat, can help you feel appreciated and valued.

- **Look for funny or humorous things:** Laughing can be a great way to reduce stress and improve your overall mood.
- **Don't try to be a perfect parent:** Remember that no one is perfect and that it's okay to make mistakes. This can help reduce stress and increase your confidence as a parent.

Case Study: David's Self-Care Journey

David was a father of two kids (one of whom had ADHD) and he found himself feeling stressed and overwhelmed in his role as a caregiver. His wife suggested that he prioritize self-care, but David initially felt guilty for even considering it. However, after a particularly difficult day, he decided to go for a walk in the park and realized that taking care of himself was essential for being the best father he could be. He started making time for himself each day, whether it was through exercise, quiet reflection, or spending quality time with loved ones.

He also began writing in a gratitude journal and started complimenting himself daily to boost his self-esteem. By prioritizing his own well-being, David was better equipped to manage his son's challenging behavior and provide him with the support he needed. David's journey showed him that self-care was not selfish, but rather essential for the well-being of his entire family. He realized that being a loving and supportive parent meant taking care of himself first.

Activity: A Self-Care Planner

A self-care planner can be a helpful tool for parents of children with ADHD to prioritize their own well-being and ensure that they are taking care of themselves. Here's a step-by-step guide on how to create your own self-care planner.

1. **Gather materials:** You will need a notebook or journal, some pens or markers, and any other materials you would like to use to decorate and personalize your planner.

2. **Create a schedule:** Start by creating a schedule for each day of the week. This should include blocks of time for self-care activities, as well as for work, family time, and other obligations.

3. **Plan your self-care activities:** Brainstorm a list of self-care activities that you enjoy and would like to incorporate into your weekly routine. Write them down in the appropriate day and time blocks.

4. **Add reminders:** Write down any important reminders or deadlines, such as doctor's appointments or meetings, so that you don't forget to take care of them.

5. **Decorate and personalize:** Use your pens, markers, and other materials to decorate and personalize your self-care planner. Make it a visual representation of your commitment to taking care of yourself.

6. **Review and revise:** Regularly review and revise your self-care planner to ensure that you are making time for self-care and other important activities.

By creating a self-care planner, you can prioritize your well-being and ensure that you are taking care of yourself, even amidst the busy and often overwhelming demands of being a parent of an ADHD preteen.

YOUR CHANCE TO HELP ANOTHER PARENT

Now that you're armed with all the tools and techniques you need to help your child navigate the world with ADHD, you're in the perfect position to help someone else.

Simply by sharing your honest opinion of this book on Amazon, you'll show new readers where they can find the information they need to navigate the same journey.

Thank you so much for your support. It's amazing what we can achieve when we work together.

CONCLUSION

This book aims to provide a comprehensive guide for parents of children with ADHD, and it covers a wide range of topics including the causes, symptoms, and treatments for ADHD. Through the various chapters, we have explored the different challenges that come with raising a child with ADHD and considered ways to approach these challenges in a positive and effective manner.

As a reader of this book, you have gained valuable insights and strategies on how to navigate the world of ADHD and help your child succeed. The key takeaways from each chapter provide a comprehensive understanding of ADHD, including the causes, symptoms, and treatments. You have learned about the various educational accommodations and therapies that can be effective in managing ADHD, and you have been introduced to various tools and techniques that can help you stay organized and communicate more effectively with your child.

One of the most essential takeaways from this book is the importance of being an informed and proactive parent. You have learned that understanding your child's ADHD is already half the battle, and that by staying informed and taking an active role in your child's care, you can help them overcome any obstacles and reach their full potential. Whether it's through researching different treatments, advocating for your child in the educational system, or simply being there for them as a supportive and loving parent, you now have the knowledge and tools necessary to help your child succeed.

Another key takeaway from this book is the importance of self-care. As a parent of a child with ADHD, it can be easy to become overwhelmed and stressed. You have learned, however, that taking care of yourself is crucial in order to be the best parent you can be. This includes taking time for yourself, seeking support from friends and family, and developing coping strategies to manage your own stress levels.

Finally, you have learned the importance of finding a support network. Whether it's through support groups, online communities, or simply connecting with other parents who understand the challenges you are facing, having a network of people who understand your situation can make all the difference in the world.

Therefore, the strategies and techniques outlined in this book provide you with the tools and knowledge necessary to help your child succeed. Whether you are a seasoned parent of a child with ADHD or just starting on this journey, this guide has provided you with valuable information that will help you and your child navigate the world of ADHD with confidence and resilience.

And, like Rhadia and Mandy who succeeded in helping their children through researching and applying similar strategies, you too can achieve great success by following the tips outlined in this guide. So, go forth, be proud of what you have accomplished, and continue to advocate for your child and yourself. Remember, understanding about your child's ADHD is already half the battle. Now, you can use the tips and techniques from this guide to help them—and yourself—traverse the situation more adeptly and confidently.

We hope you found this guide helpful and informative. If you did, we would greatly appreciate a review. Your feedback will help others who are in a similar situation and might greatly benefit from the information contained in this guide. Thank you for reading!

GLOSSARY

All glossary entries were adapted from the Merriam-Webster Dictionary (2022).

Accommodations: Changes in the environment, teaching strategies, or assessment methods that help a person with ADHD to reach their full potential.

ADHD: Attention deficit hyperactivity disorder, a neurodevelopmental disorder that is diagnosed in individuals who exhibit persistent inattention, hyperactivity, and impulsivity.

Anxiety: An emotional state characterized by feelings of nervousness, worry, and fear, often in response to everyday situations. People with ADHD may also experience anxiety.

Behavioral therapy: Behavioral therapy seeks to alter problematic behaviors by addressing underlying psychological and environmental variables. This therapy is widely used to treat a variety of mental health issues, including ADHD. It could entail teaching new skills like problem solving and time management, as well as encouraging positive behaviors while ignoring or diverting negative ones.

CDC: The Centers for Disease Control and Prevention provide data, symptoms, diagnosis, and therapy for ADHD. Additionally, parents may discover more about strategies to improve learning achievement in the classroom for children with ADHD.

Co-existing conditions: The presence of two or more mental health issues in the same person is referred to as co-existing (also called co-occurring or co-morbid). Anxiety or sadness, for example, may coexist with ADHD.

Comorbidity: A person suffering from two or more conditions at the same time.

Comprehensive assessment: A thorough examination that considers all elements that affect an individual's current challenges or difficulties in functioning. This can include factors such as behaviors, education and job abilities, family background and relationships, emotional health, social skills, traumatic experiences, and other mental health conditions. Additionally, strengths and capabilities are also evaluated. The results of this assessment serve as the foundation for making a diagnosis and creating a treatment plan.

Conduct disorder: A pattern of problematic behaviors and emotions in young individuals, characterized by aggression toward others and animals, destruction of property, deceitfulness, theft, lying, and violation of serious rules.

DSM-V: Diagnostic and Statistical Manual of Mental Disorders is a manual of the American Psychiatric Association. It explains the classification of mental health illnesses as well as the symptoms used to make a diagnosis. It is used in a variety of contexts by various health-care practitioners and insurance firms to categorize mental diseases for diagnosis and insurance purposes.

Executive functions: Cognitive processes that help with planning, organization, working memory, and self-control. People with ADHD often struggle with these skills.

Hyperactivity: A symptom of ADHD that involves excessive movement, fidgeting, and restlessness.

Hyperfocus: A concentrated, intense mental effort directed toward a specific activity, event, or subject.

Impulsivity: A symptom of ADHD that involves acting without thinking, speaking without filtering thoughts, and making impulsive decisions.

Inattention: A symptom of ADHD that involves difficulty paying attention, staying focused, and following through on tasks.

Individualized Education Plan (IEP): A written document that outlines academic goals at school as well as strategies for achieving them for children with disabilities who qualify under the IDEA. This strategy would be created based on the child's current performance level.

Medication: A treatment option for ADHD that involves the use of prescription drugs to help regulate the brain chemicals that facilitate attention and impulse control.

Mindfulness: A mental state achieved by focusing one's awareness on the present moment, while calmly acknowledging and accepting one's feelings, thoughts, and bodily sensations.

Modification: When the curriculum's standards are too high for a student to handle, modifications are made to the assignment, exam, or overall curriculum to meet the student's needs. Modifications are included in the student's IEP or Section 504 Plan.

Neurodevelopmental disorder: A condition that affects the development and function of the brain, typically resulting in difficulties with learning, behavior, and social skills.

Non-stimulant medication: A medication that has been approved for the treatment of ADHD and is typically recommended as a backup medication for those who do not respond well or do not respond at all to stimulants, are unable to handle stimulants, or have specific co-occurring mental problems.

Parent training: A type of intervention that involves educating parents about ADHD and teaching them specific strategies for managing their child's behavior and improving their family's daily routines.

Self-regulation: The process of managing and controlling one's own behavior in order to achieve one's goals.

Stimulant medication: A type of medication that increases the levels of neurotransmitters in the brain, improving attention and reducing impulsiveness in people with ADHD.

Support groups: A type of intervention that involves bringing people with ADHD and their families together to share experiences and provide emotional support.

Therapy: A type of intervention that involves working with a mental health professional to identify and change negative thought patterns and behaviors.

Working memory: A cognitive process that involves holding and manipulating information in the mind for brief periods of time. People with ADHD often struggle with working memory.

REFERENCES

A guide to self-care for parents: Why making time for yourself matters. (2020, March 31). Waterford. https://www.waterford.org/education/self-care-for-parents/

A how-to guide for getting chores done with an ADHD child. (2019, December 3). Disability Credit Canada. https://disabilitycreditcanada.com/getting-chores-done-with-your-adhd-kid-a-how-to-guide/

A list of self care tips for parents of ADHD teens. (2014, November 17). Paradigm Treatment. https://paradigmtreatment.com/list-self-care-tips-parents-adhd-teens/

Aalto University. (2022, December 20). *Virtual reality game to objectively detect ADHD.* ScienceDaily. https://www.sciencedaily.com/releases/2022/12/221220113015.htm

ADDitude Editors. (2006, October 6). *ADHD statistics.* ADDitude. https://www.additudemag.com/statistics-of-adhd/

ADDitude Editors. (2016, November 28). *10 behavior chart rewards to motivate your child.* ADDitude. https://www.additudemag.com/slideshows/reward-systems-for-kids-with-adhd-unlock-better-behavior/

ADDitude Editors. (2016, November 28). *Karate or kickball? Fencing or football? The best sports for kids with ADHD.* ADDitude. https://www.additudemag.com/slideshows/best-sports-for-kids-with-adhd/

ADDitude Editors. (2017, March 14). *What is ADHD? Everything you need to know.* ADDitude. https://www.additudemag.com/what-is-adhd-symptoms-causes-treatments/

ADDitude Editors. (2022, July 13). *Household chores for children with ADHD: Jobs that work.* ADDitude. https://www.additudemag.com/household-chores-adhd-children/

ADHD & personal hygiene. (2022, December 3). The Mini ADHD Coach. https://www.theminiadhdcoach.com/blog/adhd-and-personal-hygiene

ADHD and exercise: 8 real-world tips that will help your kids exercise better. (2021, June 29). FastBraiin. https://www.fastbraiin.com/blogs/blog/adhd-and-exercise-tips

ADHD behavior charts. (2021, August 5). Goally. https://getgoally.com/blog/adhd-behavior-charts/

ADHD. (2021). American Psychological Association. https://www.apa.org/topics/adhd#

ADHD. (2021). American Psychological Association. https://www.apa.org/topics/adhd#

Alton, N. S. (2015, September 29). *What about your special needs? Self-Care for parents of children with special needs.* Parent Map. https://www.parentmap.com/article/what-about-your-special-needs-self-care-for-parents-of-special-needs-children

Anwesha M. (2015, August 19). *11 interesting facts about human emotions that you should know.* Storypick. https://www.storypick.com/facts-about-emotions/

Armstrong, T. (2018, April 20). *Engaging creativity with ADHD.* American Institute for Learning and Human Development. https://www.institute4learning.com/2018/04/20/6-ways-to-engage-the-creative-energies-of-kids-diagnosed-with-adhd/

Attention deficit hyperactivity disorder (ADHD). (2022, February 28). American Academy of Pediatrics. https://www.aap.org/en/patient-care/attention-deficit-hyperactivity-disorder-adhd/

Attention-deficit/hyperactivity disorder (ADHD) in children. (2019). John Hopkins Medicine. https://www.hopkinsmedicine.org/health/conditions-and-diseases/adhdadd

Bae, H. W., Lee, S. Y., Kim, S. J., Shin, H. K., Choi, B. T., & Baek, J. U. (2019). Selecting effective herbal medicines for attention-deficit/hyperactivity disorder via text mining of donguibogam. *Evidence-Based Complementary and Alternative Medicine, 2019.* https://doi.org/10.1155/2019/1798364

Bailey, E. (2020, June 14). *Five tips for time management for ADHD children and teens.* Health Central. https://www.healthcentral.com/article/managing-adhd-symptoms-five-tips-for-time-management-for-children-and-teens

Belsky, G. (n.d.). *ADHD and "analysis paralysis".* Understood. https://www.understood.org/en/articles/adhd-and-analysis-paralysis

Beresin, G. (2020, January 8). *10 self-care tips for parents.* MGH Clay Center for Young Healthy Minds. https://www.mghclaycenter.org/parenting-concerns/10-self-care-tips-for-parents/

Bernstein, S. (2022, August 26). *Feingold diet for ADHD: How well does it work?.*

WebMD. https://www.webmd.com/add-adhd/childhood-adhd/what-is-the-feingold-diet

Bertin, M. (2020, August 7). *Calm starts at home: How to teach emotional regulation skills.* ADDitude. https://www.additudemag.com/emotional-regulation-skills-adhd-children/

Bestquotes. (2022, May 30). *Taking a break quotes.* Terse Sayings. https://tersesayings.com/taking-a-break-quotes/

Bhandari, S. (2022, December 16). *Parenting dos and don'ts: ADHD and discipline.* WebMD. https://www.webmd.com/add-adhd/childhood-adhd/ss/slideshow-adhd-parenting-discipline-tips

Bisht, A. (2018, June 7). *Here's how Ryan Gosling's life turned around after being evaluated for ADHD in his childhood.* Desimartini. https://www.desimartini.com/news/martini-shots/entertainment/the-journey-towards-the-success-of-ryan-gosling-article86871.htm

Board, A. E. (2006, October 6). *The homework system that really works.* ADDitude. https://www.additudemag.com/adhd-and-homework-get-it-done-strategies-for-students/

Board, A. E. (2016, November 28). *In this house, we don't tolerate bullying.* ADDitude. https://www.additudemag.com/slideshows/no-more-bullying-strategies-for-adhd-kids/

Braaten, E. (n.d.). *Is ADHD hereditary.* Understood. https://www.understood.org/en/articles/is-adhd-hereditary

Brady, C. (2021, May 21). *Social skills for kids and tweens with ADHD.* ADDitude. https://www.additudemag.com/how-to-tease-proof-your-preteen/

Broadbent, E. (2022, December 13). *Inattentive ADHD: Insights from a tween with ADD.* ADDitude. https://www.additudemag.com/inattentive-adhd-tween-personal-perspective/

Castle, J. (2021, July 9). *ADHD nutrition: A healthy diet for kids.* The Nourished Child. https://thenourishedchild.com/healthy-adhd-diet-kids/

Causes—attention deficit hyperactivity disorder (ADHD). (2021, December 24). National Health Service. https://www.nhs.uk/conditions/attention-deficit-hyperactivity-disorder-adhd/causes/

Chowdhury, M. R. (2019, August 13). *What is emotion regulation? 6 emotional skills and strategies.* PositivePsychology.com. https://positivepsychology.com/emotion-regulation/#regulation

CNN Editor Team (n.d.). *Did Leonardo da Vinci have ADHD? Academics say he did*. CNN. https://edition.cnn.com/style/article/leonardo-da-vinci-adhd-scli-intl/index.html

Cohen, M. (2018, October 3). *Can you treat ADHD without drugs?*. WebMD. https://www.webmd.com/add-adhd/childhood-adhd/can-you-treat-adhd-without-drugs

Cohen, M. (2022, July 25). *Can you treat ADHD without drugs?*. WebMD. https://www.webmd.com/add-adhd/childhood-adhd/can-you-treat-adhd-without-drugs#

Cooney, M. (2022, January). *Working with teachers to help your ADHD child be comfortable at school*. Study.com. https://study.com/blog/working-with-teachers-to-help-your-adhd-child-be-comfortable-at-school.html

Create chore chart for kids with ADHD or autism that work. (2022, November 22). Goally. https://getgoally.com/blog/create-chore-charts-for-kids-with-adhd-or-autism-that-work/

Daley, J. (2019, June 5). *New study suggests Leonardo da Vinci had ADHD*. Smithsonian Magazine. https://www.smithsonianmag.com/smart-news/new-study-suggests-da-vinci-had-adhd-180972359/

Darabi, Z., Vasmehjani, A. A., Darand, M., Sangouni, A. A., & Hosseinzadeh, M. (2021). *Adherence to Mediterranean diet and attention-deficit/hyperactivity disorder in children: A case control study*. Clinical Nutrition ESPEN. https://doi.org/10.1016/j.clnesp.2021.11.014

Data and statistics about ADHD. (2021, September 23). Centers for Disease Control and Prevention. https://www.cdc.gov/ncbddd/adhd/data.html

Day, N. (2019, July 6). *How to help children with ADHD develop problem-solving skills*. Raising an Extraordinary Person. https://hes-extraordinary.com/problem-solving-skills-adhd

DeSantis, M. (n.d.). *Celebrities with dyslexia, ADHD, and dyscalculia*. Understood. https://www.understood.org/en/articles/success-stories-celebrities-with-dyslexia-adhd-and-dyscalculia

Dowd, K. E. (2017, April 28). *Michael phelps opens up about ADHD struggles*. Sports Illustrated. https://www.si.com/olympics/2017/04/28/michael-phelps-opens-about-adhd-struggles-teacher-told-me-id-never-amount-anything

Drechsler, R., Brem, S., Brandeis, D., Grünblatt, E., Berger, G., & Walitza, S. (2020). ADHD: Current concepts and treatments in children and adolescents. *Neuropediatrics, 51*(5), 315–335. https://doi.org/10.1055/s-0040-1701658

Dresden, D. (2022, April 27). *Natural remedies for ADHD: Options and risks.* Medical News Today. https://www.medicalnewstoday.com/articles/315239#help-for-adults-with-adhd

Dutton, J. (2007, March 20). *How swimming saved Michael Phelps: An ADHD story.* ADDitude. https://www.additudemag.com/michael-phelps-adhd-advice-from-the-olympians-mom/

Emma. (2020, April 11). *30-day at-home self-care challenge.* Our Mindful Life. https://www.ourmindfullife.com/at-home-self-care-calendar/

Emotion regulation in teens with ADHD. (n.d.). CHADD. https://chadd.org/attention-article/emotion-regulation-in-teens-with-adhd/

Emotion regulation. (2019). Psychology Today. https://www.psychologytoday.com/us/basics/emotion-regulation

Faraone, S. V., & Larsson, H. (2018). Genetics of attention deficit hyperactivity disorder. *Molecular Psychiatry, 24*(4), 562–575. https://doi.org/10.1038/s41380-018-0070-0

5 tips for helping children with ADHD deal with aggression. (2019, September 18). HOPE Therapy and Wellness Center. https://www.hopetherapyandwellness.com/blog/115541-5-tips-for-helping-children-with-adhd-deal-with-aggression

5 top tips for getting your child with ADHD to do their "chores". (2022, January 2). ADHD Done Differently. https://adhddonedifferently.com.au/2022/01/02/5-top-tips-for-getting-your-child-with-adhd-to-do-their-chores/

Forbes, S. E. (2017, October 16). *What is my ADHD child's executive function age?.* Grace Under Pressure . https://www.graceunderpressure.blog/2017/10/16/what-is-my-childs-executive-function-age/

Glossary of terms. (n.d.). CHADD. https://chadd.org/about-adhd/glossary-of-terms/

Griffin, R. M. (2022, January 23). *Ways to study better.* WebMD. https://www.webmd.com/add-adhd/childhood-adhd/study-better

Grushkin, B. (2021, November 14). *Chores for ADHD kids : Strategies to get the work done.* Fuzzy Mama. https://www.fuzzymama.com/how-to-get-adhd-child-to-do-chores/

Guest Author. (2021, May 3). *Helping children with ADHD focus without medication: 7 tips for parents.* Resources to Recover. https://www.rtor.org/2021/05/03/helping-children-with-adhd-focus-without-medication-tips-for-parents/

Haan, E., Westmoreland, K. E., Schellhas, L., Sallis, H. M., Taylor, G., Zuccolo,

L., & Munafò, M. R. (2022). Prenatal smoking, alcohol and caffeine exposure and offspring externalizing disorders: A systematic review and meta-analysis. *Addiction, 117*(10), 2602-2613. https://doi.org/10.1111/add.15858

Hallowell, E. (2013, October 24). *Anger is important—but only when it's managed.* ADDitude. https://www.additudemag.com/anger-management-techniques-for-children-with-adhd/

Hasan, S. (2017). *ADHD and school (for parents).* Kids Health. https://kidshealth.org/en/parents/adhd-school.html

Hasan, S. (2018). *ADHD (for parents).* Kids Health. https://kidshealth.org/en/parents/adhd.html

Help your child make and keep friends. (n.d.). CHADD. https://chadd.org/adhd-weekly/help-your-child-make-and-keep-friends/

Herskovitz, B. (2016). *Does my child have ADHD? 3 minute test & screening.* Psycom. https://www.psycom.net/does-my-child-have-adhd

Holland, K. (2018, May 30). *ADHD by the numbers: Facts, statistics, and you.* Healthline Media. https://www.healthline.com/health/adhd/facts-statistics-infographic#fast-facts

Is ADHD related to creativity?. (2021, June). CHADD. https://chadd.org/attention-article/is-adhd-related-to-creativity/

Jacobson, R. (2023, January 26). *School success kit for kids with ADHD.* Child Mind Institute. https://childmind.org/article/school-success-kit-for-kids-with-adhd/

Kelly, K. (n.d.). *ADHD and creativity.* Understood. https://www.understood.org/en/articles/adhd-and-creativity-what-you-need-to-know

Key, A. P. (2021, April 7). *ADHD in children: Managing moods and emotions.* WebMD. https://www.webmd.com/add-adhd/adhd-children-mood-swings

Klynn, B. (2021, June 22). *Emotional regulation: Skills, exercises, and strategies.* BetterUp. https://www.betterup.com/blog/emotional-regulation-skills

Knopik, V. S., Marceau, K., Bidwell, L. C., Palmer, R. H. C., Smith, T. F., Todorov, A., Evans, A. S., & Heath, A. C. (2016). Smoking during pregnancy and ADHD risk: A genetically informed, multiple-rater approach. *American Journal of Medical Genetics Part B: Neuropsychiatric Genetics, 171*(7), 971–981. https://doi.org/10.1002/ajmg.b.32421

Koder, M. (2020, March 3). *How to help your ADHD child make & keep friends.* Revibe Tech. https://blog.revibetech.com/how-to-help-your-adhd-child-make-keep-friends

LaBianca, J. (2022, December 2). *10 silent signs your child is being bullied.* Reader's Digest. https://www.rd.com/list/bullying-signs/

Lee-Kruger, K. (2019, December 27). *Music and the brain: How piano lessons saved my ADHD child.* ADDitudemag. https://www.additudemag.com/music-and-the-brain-adhd-piano/

Li, P. (2019, September 15). *The science of emotional regulation.* Parenting for Brain. https://www.parentingforbrain.com/self-regulation-toddler-temper-tantrums/

Life skills education school handbook prevention of noncommunicable diseases. (2020). World Health Organization. https://apps.who.int/iris/rest/bitstreams/1276896/retrieve

Livingstone, L. T., Coventry, W. L., Corley, R. P., Willcutt, E. G., Samuelsson, S., Olson, R. K., & Byrne, B. (2016). Does the environment have an enduring effect on ADHD? A longitudinal study of monozygotic twin differences in children. *Journal of Abnormal Child Psychology, 44*(8), 1487–1501. https://doi.org/10.1007/s10802-016-0145-9

Lockett, E. (2022, March 14). *What are the most common signs of ADHD?* Healthline. https://www.healthline.com/health/adhd/signs#signs-in-children

Lopatin, A. (2022, February 15). *ADHD and bullying (part 1): How to help kids with ADHD recognize, respond to and prevent bullying.* Dr. Sharon Saline. https://drsharonsaline.com/2022/02/15/adhd-and-bullying-part-1-how-to-help-kids-with-adhd-recognize-respond-to-and-prevent-bullying/

Lovering, N. (2022, May 18). *ADHD and emotions: Relationship and tips to manage.* Healthline. https://www.healthline.com/health/adhd/emotional-regulation

Low, K. (2019). *Negative ADHD behaviors can impact the social skills of children.* Verywell Mind. https://www.verywellmind.com/how-to-improve-social-skills-in-children-with-adhd-20727

Low, K. (2021, January 5). *How people with ADHD can cope with hypersensitivity in situations.* Verywell Mind. https://www.verywellmind.com/sensitivities-and-adhd-20473

Low, K. (2022, April 19). *Children with ADHD need structure in their lives to stay focused.* Verywell Mind. https://www.verywellmind.com/why-is-structure-important-for-kids-with-adhd-20747

Lynn, M. (2018, November 28). *How to teach ADHD kids potty training.* Hello

Motherhood. https://www.hellomotherhood.com/how-to-teach-adhd-kids-potty-training-4480567.html

Macmillan Education. (2019, August 9). *Why are life skills important?* Macmillan English. https://www.macmillanenglish.com/us/blog-resources/article/why-are-life-skills-important

Making a feelings thermometer. (2016, April 27). Coping Skills for Kids. https://copingskillsforkids.com/blog/2016/4/27/making-a-feelings-thermometer

Mandriota, M. (2021, October 14). *The 7 best natural remedies for ADHD.* Psych Central. https://psychcentral.com/adhd/home-remedies-for-adhd#benefits

Mandriota, M. (2022, April 12). *ADHD and social skills: What to know.* Psych Central. https://psychcentral.com/adhd/adhd-social-skills#different-ages

Marcin, A. (2019, September 10). *Creating an effective behavior chart: Types, treats, tips & more.* Healthline. https://www.healthline.com/health/parenting/behavior-chart#types

Margolis, C. (2021, April 30). *My daughter is being bullied at school: Guest blogs.* ADDitudemag. https://www.additudemag.com/my-daughter-is-being-bullied-at-school/

Marner, K. (2010, November 8). *How fidgeting has helped my child's ADHD.* ADDitude. https://www.additudemag.com/tell-us-how-fidgeting-has-helped-your-addadhd-child-and-win-a-set-of-classroom-friendly-fidgets/

Marner, K. (2021, July 19). *Sensory issues and hygiene in ADHD children.* ADDitudemag. https://www.additudemag.com/when-sensory-processing-disorder-symptoms-get-in-the-way-of-good-hygiene/

Marner, K. (2022a, March 12). *ADHD children and gymnastics.* ADDitudemag. https://www.additudemag.com/can-my-adhd-daughter-focus-while-doing-gymnastics/

Marner, K. (2022b, March 19). *Parenting ADHD children blog: Caring for your own health.* ADDitudemag. https://www.additudemag.com/when-mom-neglects-her-own-health/

Masters, T. (2022, April 22). *The power of rewards for kids with ADHD.* Edge Foundation. https://edgefoundation.org/the-power-of-rewards-for-kids-with-adhd/

Matheis, L. (2022, February 28). *How to set up a daily routine for your child with ADHD.* Joon. https://www.joonapp.io/post/how-to-set-up-a-daily-routine-for-your-child-with-adhd

Matthews-King, A. (2019, May 23). *Leonardo da Vinci may have had ADHD, leading professor says*. The Independent. https://www.independent.co.uk/news/health/leonardo-da-vinci-adhd-health-mona-lisa-a8927641.html

May, T., & Stubbs, S. (2022, September 15). *Friendships: Children and pre-teens with attention deficit hyperactivity disorder (ADHD)*. Raising Children Network. https://raisingchildren.net.au/school-age/development/adhd/friendships-children-pre-teens-adhd#finding-friends-for-children-and-pre-teens-with-adhd-nav-title

McArthur, K. (2019, January 8). *Self-care strategies for parents of kids with ADHD*. Today's Parent. https://www.todaysparent.com/family/special-needs/simple-self-care-tips-for-parents-of-kids-with-adhd/

McAully, L. (2023, January 5). *"I'm the mum of an 11-year-old with ADHD and I hate the diagnosis."*. MamaMia. https://www.mamamia.com.au/parenting-daughter-adhd/

Mehren, A., Reichert, M., Coghill, D., Müller, H. H. O., Braun, N., & Philipsen, A. (2020). Physical exercise in attention deficit hyperactivity disorder – evidence and implications for the treatment of borderline personality disorder. *Borderline Personality Disorder and Emotion Dysregulation, 7*(1). https://doi.org/10.1186/s40479-019-0115-2

Merriam-Webster dictionary. (2022). Merriam-Webster. https://www.merriam-webster.com/

Morin, A. (2015, January 12). *7 ways to help an angry child*. Verywell Family. https://www.verywellfamily.com/ways-to-help-an-angry-child-1094976

Morin, A. (2019). *15 self-care strategies for busy parents*. Verywell Family. https://www.verywellfamily.com/self-care-for-parents-4178010

Morin, A. (2021, April 25). *How to help overly emotional kids deal with their big feelings*. Verywell Family. https://www.verywellfamily.com/how-to-help-an-overly-emotional-child-4157594

Morin, A. (n.d.-a). *5 tips to help kids follow a schedule or routine*. Understood. https://www.understood.org/en/articles/tips-child-stick-to-schedule

Morin, A. (n.d.-b). *8 common myths about ADHD*. Understood. https://www.understood.org/en/articles/common-myths-about-adhd

Morin, A. (n.d.-c). *ADHD and social skills*. Understood. https://www.understood.org/en/articles/5-ways-adhd-can-affect-social-skills

Mrug, S., Molina, B. S. G., Hoza, B., Gerdes, A. C., Hinshaw, S. P., Hechtman, L., & Arnold, L. E. (2012). Peer rejection and friendships in children with attention-deficit/hyperactivity disorder: Contributions to long-term outcomes. *Journal of Abnormal Child Psychology, 40*(6), 1013–1026. https://doi.org/10.1007/s10802-012-9610-2

Myers, R. (n.d.). *10 concentration and focus building techniques for children with ADHD.* Empowering Parents. https://www.empoweringparents.com/article/5-simple-concentration-building-techniques-for-kids-with-adhd/

Myths and misunderstandings. (2018). CHADD. https://chadd.org/about-adhd/myths-and-misunderstandings/

Newmark, S. Y. (2020, October 13). *The big 3: How nutrition, exercise & sleep curb ADHD in children.* ADDitude. https://www.additudemag.com/natural-remedies-adhd-children-nutrition-exercise-sleep/

Nicholson, S. (2020, April 24). *ADHD: Expecting more from chores—ADHD care in pediatric patients.* Med Page Today. https://www.medpagetoday.com/resource-centers/adhd-care-pediatric-patients/adhd-expecting-more-chores/2829

Nigg, J. (2018, February 15). *How ADHD amplifies emotions.* ADDitude. https://www.additudemag.com/emotional-dysregulation-adhd-video/

Orchid Centre. (2020, August 4). *Executive function age vs. chronological age: Where does my child fall?.* Orchid ADHD. https://orchidadhd.com/2020/08/04/executive-function-age-vs-chronological-age-where-does-my-child-fall/

Oxford Learning. (2017, January 2). *10 homework & study tips for kids with ADD/ADHD.* Oxford Learning. https://www.oxfordlearning.com/10-add-adhd-study-tips/

Peterson, T. J. (n.d.). *What does an ADHD reward system have to do with discipline?* Healthy Place. https://www.healthyplace.com/parenting/discipline/what-does-an-adhd-reward-system-have-to-do-with-discipline

Pfiffner, L. J., & Haack, L. M. (2014). Behavior management for school-aged children with ADHD. *Child and Adolescent Psychiatric Clinics of North America, 23*(4), 731–746. https://doi.org/10.1016/j.chc.2014.05.014

Pietrangelo, A. (2020, June 4). *Diet tips and snack ideas for kids with ADHD.* Healthline. https://www.healthline.com/health/adhd/diet-tips-snack-ideas#tips

Porter, E. (2017, October 13). *Parenting tips for ADHD: Do's and don'ts.* Healthline Media. https://www.healthline.com/health/adhd/parenting-tips#what-not-to-do

Posner, J. (2006, October 6). *9 ADHD myths and fallacies that perpetuate stigma.*

ADDitude. https://www.additudemag.com/adhd-myths-and-facts-learn-the-truth-about-attention-deficit/

Predina, A. (2021, July 22). *My energetic kid: Channeling ADHD hyperactivity.* ADDitudemag. https://www.additudemag.com/energetic-kid-activities-adhd/

Preiato, D. (2021, October 19). *ADHD and exercise: What you need to know.* Healthline. https://www.healthline.com/health/fitness/adhd-and-exercise

Quinn, P. O., & Madhoo, M. (2014). A review of attention-deficit/hyperactivity disorder in women and girls. *The Primary Care Companion for CNS Disorders, 16*(3). https://doi.org/10.4088/pcc.13r01596

Ramsay, R. (2021, June 5). *Taking breaks, avoiding distractions, and adults with ADHD.* Psychology Today. https://www.psychologytoday.com/us/blog/rethinking-adult-adhd/202106/taking-breaks-avoiding-distractions-and-adults-with-adhd

Reinberg, S. (2013, October 13). *Kids with ADHD often prone to bowel problems: Study—consumer health news.* Healthday. https://consumer.healthday.com/kids-health-information-23/attention-deficit-disorder-adhd-news-50/kids-with-adhd-often-prone-to-bowel-problems-study-681235.html

Resnick, A. (2022, May 10). *ADHD diet for kids.* Verywell Mind. https://www.verywellmind.com/adhd-diet-for-kids-foods-to-eat-and-foods-to-avoid-5225681

Robinson, S. (2014, October 6). *How to create a consistent routine for kids with ADHD.* Look! We're Learning! https://www.lookwerelearning.com/creating-adhd-daily-routine-for-kids/

Roybal, B. (2008, May 13). *ADHD diet and nutrition.* WebMD. https://www.webmd.com/add-adhd/adhd-diets

Saline, S. (2020, December 16). *5 parent self-care ideas: Parenting ADHD in a pandemic.* Dr. Sharon Saline. https://drsharonsaline.com/2020/12/16/5-parent-self-care-ideas-parenting-a-child-or-teen-with-adhd-in-a-pandemic/

Saline, S. (2022, April 1). *The one word you must remove from your vocabulary when parenting kids with ADHD.* Your Tango. https://www.yourtango.com/family/parenting-kids-with-adhd

Saranga, V. (2016, June 7). *ADHD: Teaching your child to regulate their emotions.* LinkedIn. https://www.linkedin.com/pulse/adhd-teaching-your-child-regulate-emotions-vinay-saranga-md

Schonwald, A. (2011, April 29). *Toilet training: Strategies for success in children with developmental disabilities.* Consultant 360. https://www.consultant360. com/articles/toilet-training-strategies-success-children-developmental-disabilities

Schoppe-Sullivan, S. (2017, February 3). *Dads are more involved in parenting, yes, but moms still put in more work.* The Conversation. https://theconversa tion.com/dads-are-more-involved-in-parenting-yes-but-moms-still-put-in-more-work-72026

Self-Care for parents and carers. (n.d.). Anna Freud Centre. https://www. annafreud.org/parents-and-carers/self-care-for-parents-and-carers/

Self-care for parents. (n.d.). UNICEF. Retrieved February 5, 2023, from https:// www.unicef.org/parenting/mental-health/parent-self-care-tips

Shannon, M. (2018, July 7). *Hygiene in ADHD kids: Teaching independence.* Miss Shannon's Cat Farm. http://cat-farm.com/hygiene/

Signs your child is being bullied—tip sheet. (n.d.). STOMP Out Bullying. https:// www.stompoutbullying.org/tip-sheet-signs-your-child-being-bullied

Sinfield, J. (2019). *ADHD symptoms you should be on the lookout for.* Verywell Mind. https://www.verywellmind.com/adhd-symptoms-4157281

Sinn, N. (2008). Nutritional and dietary influences on attention deficit hyper-activity disorder. *Nutrition Reviews, 66*(10), 558–568. https://doi.org/10.1111/j.1753-4887.2008.00107.xSmith, J. (2021, June 29). ADHD and creativity: 5 key tips on encouraging creativity in your child. FastBraiin. https://www.fastbraiin.com/blogs/blog/adhd-and-creativity

6 indoor exercise ideas for kids with ADHD. (2021, February 8). Next Step 4 ADHD. https://nextstep4adhd.com/6-indoor-exercise-ideas-for-kids-with-adhd/

Smith, L. (2021, December 14). *What to do if your child with ADHD won't eat.* GoodRx Health. https://www.goodrx.com/conditions/adhd/childhood-adhd-picky-eating

Smith, M. (2019). *ADHD and school.* Help Guide. https://www.helpguide.org/ articles/add-adhd/attention-deficit-disorder-adhd-and-school.htm

Smith, M., Robinson, L., & Segal, J. (2019, January 10). *ADHD in children.* Help Guide. https://www.helpguide.org/articles/add-adhd/attention-deficit-disorder-adhd-in-children.htm

Snyders, E. (2016, July 23). *Act your {executive} age! Are you expecting too much out of your ADHD child?.* Honestly ADHD. https://honestlyadhd.com/adhd-executive-age/

South, F. (2022a, March 13). *ADHD hyperfocus: Completing schoolwork on time.* ADDitudemag. https://www.additudemag.com/adhd-supergirl/

South, F. (2022b, March 17). *My daughter's ADHD rage and frustration, explained.* ADDitudemag. https://www.additudemag.com/adhd-rage-explained/

Sutherby, R. (2022, February 28). *ADHD and decision making: Symptoms, tips, and more.* Psych Central. https://psychcentral.com/adhd/adults-adhd-tips-to-make-good-decisions#strategies-and-tips

Tagliareni, L. (n.d.). *ADHD and sleep problems.* Understood. https://www.understood.org/en/articles/how-adhd-affects-kids-sleep-and-what-you-can-do

Teach.com. (2020, April 3). *Resources for teaching kids about emotional regulation and meditation.* Teach.com. https://teach.com/resources/teaching-children-emotional-regulation/

The importance of a daily schedule for kids with ADHD—back to school series. (2019, August 20). ADHD Ireland. https://adhdireland.ie/the-importance-of-a-daily-schedule-for-kids-with-adhd-back-to-school-series/

The Understood Team. (n.d.-a). *6 simple ways to improve your child's focus.* Understood. https://www.understood.org/en/articles/how-to-improve-focus-in-kids

The Understood Team. (n.d.-b). *How Michael Phelps' ADHD helped him make Olympic history.* Understood. https://www.understood.org/en/articles/celebrity-spotlight-how-michael-phelps-adhd-helped-him-make-olympic-history

Thornbury, L. (2017, February 20). *25 quotes about parenting A child with disabilities.* Forever in Mom Genes. https://www.foreverinmomgenes.com/2017/02/19/25-quotes-about-special-needs-parenting/

Treatment of ADHD. (2022b, August 9). Centers for Disease Control and Prevention. https://www.cdc.gov/ncbddd/adhd/treatment.html

Treatment—attention deficit hyperactivity disorder (ADHD). (2019). National Health Service. https://www.nhs.uk/conditions/attention-deficit-hyperactivity-disorder-adhd/treatment/

Vaccines have no role in ADHD. (2019). CHADD. https://chadd.org/adhd-weekly/vaccines-have-no-role-in-adhd/

Vernadakis, G., & Vogt, C. (2023, January 4). *ADHD resources and glossary of terms.* Everyday Health. https://www.everydayhealth.com/adhd/resources-glossary-terms/

Villines, Z. (2021, June 29). *What to do if a child with ADHD cannot sleep: 6 tips.*

Medical News Today. https://www.medicalnewstoday.com/articles/adhd-child-sleep

Vrouvas, M. (2023). *Helping your ADHD child cope with being bullied.* Study.com. https://study.com/blog/helping-your-adhd-child-cope-with-being-bullied.html

Wait, M. (2015, May 12). *How to recognize ADHD symptoms at every age.* WebMD. https://www.webmd.com/add-adhd/childhood-adhd/adhd-symptoms-age

Watson, S. (2021, June 14). *Teens and tweens: ADHD and time-management skills.* WebMD. https://www.webmd.com/add-adhd/childhood-adhd/teens-tweens-adhd-time-management

Wedge, M. (2016, August 8). *What we can learn from Michael Phelps about ADHD.* Psychology Today. https://www.psychologytoday.com/us/blog/suffer-the-children/201608/what-we-can-learn-michael-phelps-about-adhd

Wexelblatt, R. (2022, May 19). *The social executive function skills that elude kids with ADHD.* ADDitude. https://www.additudemag.com/social-skills-for-kids-friendships-adhd/

What is ADHD?. (2022). Centers for Disease Control and Prevention. https://www.cdc.gov/ncbddd/adhd/facts.html

What is attention deficit hyperactivity disorder?. (2008, September 18). WebMD. https://www.webmd.com/add-adhd/childhood-adhd/attention-deficit-hyperactivity-disorder-adhd

What is life skills education & why it is important?. (2021, April 2). Digital Class Educational World. https://www.digitalclassworld.com/blog/life-skills-education/

Why you should really worry about your ADHD kid's dreadful social skills. (2020, November 6). Start Here Parents. https://startthereparents.com/social-skills-kids-adhd/

Wilcox, K. (2022, May 9). *The link between creativity and ADHD.* Psychology Today. https://www.psychologytoday.com/intl/blog/mythbusting-adhd/202205/the-link-between-creativity-and-adhd

Wooster, C. B. (2020, September 16). *Put the oxygen mask on yourself first! A self-care analogy.* LinkedIn. https://www.linkedin.com/pulse/put-oxygen-mask-yourself-first-self-care-analogy-cyrena-wooster-ivie

Zhang, F., Liu, K., An, P., You, C., Teng, L., & Liu, Q. (2017). Music therapy for attention deficit hyperactivity disorder (ADHD) in children and adolescents. *Cochrane Database of Systematic Reviews, 2017(5)*. https://doi.org/10.1002/14651858.cd010032.pub2

IMAGE REFERENCES

Black ice. (2018). *Alarm clock lying on multicolored surface* [Image]. Pexels. https://www.pexels.com/photo/alarm-clock-lying-on-multicolored-surface-1314544/

Burton, K. (2021). *Desperate screaming young boy* [Image]. Pexels. https://www.pexels.com/photo/desperate-screaming-young-boy-6624327/

Cameron, J. M. (2020). *Boy in yellow crew neck t-shirt sitting on chair* [Image]. Pexels. https://www.pexels.com/photo/boy-in-yellow-crew-neck-t-shirt-sitting-on-chair-4144101/

Cottonbro Studio. (2020). *Mom and daughter eating cake on brown wooden table* [Image]. Pexels. https://www.pexels.com/photo/mom-and-daughter-eating-cake-on-brown-wooden-table-3992140/

Cottonbro studio. (2021). *A young woman ironing clothes* [Image]. Pexels. https://www.pexels.com/photo/a-young-woman-ironing-clothes-7705344/

Danilyuk, P. (2020). *Woman in white lab coat listening to a girl and writing down notes* [Image]. Pexels. https://www.pexels.com/photo/woman-in-white-lab-coat-listening-to-a-girl-and-writing-down-notes-5998448/

Fring, G. (2020). *Woman giving pills to man* [Image]. Pexels. https://www.pexels.com/photo/woman-giving-pills-to-man-5934485/

Holmes, K. (2020). *Cheerful black teacher with diverse schoolkids* [Image]. Pexels. https://www.pexels.com/photo/cheerful-black-teacher-with-diverse-schoolkids-5905918/

Kampus Production. (2021). *Children playing football together* [Image]. Pexels. https://www.pexels.com/photo/children-playing-football-together-8813560/

Kindel Media. (2021). *Woman in blue shirt talking to a young man in white shirt* [Image]. Pexels. https://www.pexels.com/photo/woman-in-blue-shirt-talking-to-a-young-man-in-white-shirt-8550841/

Monstera. (2020). *Cute girl thinking over bright puzzle cube* [Image]. Pexels. https://www.pexels.com/photo/cute-girl-thinking-over-bright-puzzle-cube-5063561/

Nilov, M. (2021). *Sad boy in gray sweater sitting on the floor* [Image]. Pexels.

https://www.pexels.com/photo/sad-boy-in-gray-sweater-sitting-on-the-floor-7929419/

Ogino, K. (2020). *Young asian woman piggybacking smiling daughter while exercising at home* [Image]. Pexels. https://www.pexels.com/photo/young-asian-woman-piggybacking-smiling-daughter-while-exercising-at-home-5094677/

Phan, H. (2019). *Man reading a book* [Image]. Pexels. https://www.pexels.com/photo/man-reading-a-book-2277385/

Pixabay. (2017). *Person behind books* [Image]. Pexels. https://www.pexels.com/photo/adult-blur-books-close-up-261909/

Podrez, A. (2021). *A girl sleeping on a bed* [Image]. Pexels. https://www.pexels.com/photo/a-girl-sleeping-on-a-bed-7504925/

RODNAE Productions. (2021). *A girl sitting lonely by herself in the classroom* [Image]. Pexels. https://www.pexels.com/photo/a-girl-sitting-lonely-by-herself-in-the-classroom-6936478/

RODNAE Productions. (2021). *Children sitting at the park* [Image]. Pexels. https://www.pexels.com/photo/children-sitting-at-the-park-8033808/

Shuraeva, A. (2021). *Children holding papers with painted letters* [Image]. Pexels. https://www.pexels.com/photo/children-holding-papers-with-painted-letters-6964738/

Winstead, T. (2021). *ADHD Text* [Image]. Pexels. https://www.pexels.com/photo/adhd-text-8378728/

CPSIA information can be obtained
at www.ICGtesting.com
Printed in the USA
LVHW020329260523
748109LV00002B/148

9 798987 950500